WILD ANIMALS OF BRITAIN

this is a
SIGNPOST
book

MOLE

HEDGEHOG

COMMON SHREW

PYGMY SHREW

WATER SHREW

PLATE 1

WILD ANIMALS
OF BRITAIN

Written and Illustrated by

KEITH SHACKLETON

THOMAS NELSON AND SONS LTD
LONDON EDINBURGH PARIS MELBOURNE JOHANNESBURG
TORONTO AND NEW YORK

THOMAS NELSON AND SONS LTD
Parkside Works Edinburgh 9
36 Park Street London W1
117 Latrobe Street Melbourne C1

THOMAS NELSON AND SONS (AFRICA) (Pty) LTD
P.O. Box 9881 Johannesburg

THOMAS NELSON AND SONS (CANADA) LTD
81 Curlew Drive Don Mills Ontario

THOMAS NELSON AND SONS
18 East 41st Street New York 17, N.Y.

SOCIÉTÉ FRANÇAISE D'ÉDITIONS NELSON
97 rue Monge Paris 5

First published 1959
Reprinted 1964

Printed in Great Britain by
Thomas Nelson (Printers) Ltd, London and Edinburgh

PREFACE

Had this book been on a more technical plane it would have been called *Mammals in Britain*. The choice of its name, however, was intended to give a hint to its contents, which if more complete would have needed a very different author.

I have sought to present just a few of the points about the lives of wild animals which may interest people, in the full knowledge that if their enquiry and enthusiasm should wish to go further there are many resources of reference available from those far more qualified to write about them. In truth, were it not for my wish to draw the animals in this book, it might have been hard to find courage enough to set down the text.

My own shortcomings in knowledge of this subject have offered the advantage of being able to guess what others might want to know, believing that those who think of warm-blooded, fur-covered creatures as animals rather than mammals, are likely to be at first more interested in their breeding, their food, and where to find them than in the obscure points of their biology. The study of anything in nature, because of its endlessness, must have a small beginning.

My sincere gratitude is extended to many sources of help. In particular must be mentioned the facilities of the British Museum of Natural History and for its permission to reprint T. C. S. Morrison Scott's check-list of British Mammals; the Zoological Society of London and the researches of Dr. L. Harrison Matthews upon which I have freely drawn; and the studies of a great many other zoologists. I am grateful also to my wife for every form of help and encouragement, even to the extent of nurturing mice in our kitchen believing that their presence might make the drawings more authentic.

HOUSE MOUSE

CONTENTS

CONTENTS

CONTENTS

GREY SQUIRREL

COLOUR PLATES

xi

COLOUR PLATES

FOREWORD

By accepting the word 'animal' as a scientific classification separating all living things from plants, the word 'mammal' has to be used to name the creatures in this book, and this will call for some sort of definition of the word itself.

In the scale of evolution mammals are the most advanced and specialised of animals and include Man. They are all warm-blooded and suckle their young, and most of them are covered with fur. But there are many smaller and less definite distinctions which make it difficult to wrap it up in one tidy definition that leaves out no loose ends nor contradictions.

Mammals are subdivided into sixteen orders of which only eight have representatives in the British Isles. Highest among these orders are the Primates which include Man.

From the point of view of study in their natural environment, mammals are not easy. Birds are familiar sights and completely accepted, but mammals because of their very concealment and retiring ways tend to be regarded as rarities whilst in fact they are everywhere and close by in surprisingly large numbers. When seen they will always draw comment, from the magnificent park deer to the rat that scuttles across the road in the headlights. Only a few of them can be carefully watched for prolonged periods, and much of their hidden life would be still unknown were it not for painstaking field work, laboratory study, and varied captivity over many years. The fruits of this research and the knowledge it has brought will always add interest and further enchantment to the sight of an animal in the wild.

It is worth mentioning one or two facts common to all mammals to avoid much repetition later on. Each Order has been taken separately and the typical points common to all its members mentioned. This has been particularly necessary with animals such as the bat, the physical characteristics and ways of which are all so much alike, with more or less their only differences being details of size, shape and colour and in the times of their flight.

One of the most important points concerning all mammals is that of colour. There is a great deal more colour variation among mammals than most other creatures, and it is therefore difficult to be fully explicit in the colours mentioned under their various descriptions. The normal tendency is that they are all shaded darker above than below; this is part of a general pattern of concealment, the darker upper parts compensating for the light which would normally fall from above; at the same time the light underparts offset the shadow which would normally fall across them, and as a result the animal tends to appear flat and less obvious against a natural background.

A second general note concerns the varying habits of the same species. In different parts of the country animals behave in different ways, gearing their habits to the nature of the country and often behaving differently in consequence. Such behaviour is very noticeable in animals like the rabbit, whose range extends from the rocky hills to the fertile lowlands. House mice in homes will have a life cycle far removed from the same animal which has elected to live out of doors. It should be remembered that the spread of small mammals such as the rodents is inevitably slow; they have none of the advantages of birds in their ease of movement and migration, and there is nothing unusual about a single mouse being born, growing up, mating, breeding, and dying in the confines of a single sack of grain.

DOLPHINS

In recent years there have been a great many introductions of species alien to Britain both by escape and by intention. All these are included on the check-list because it is important that any mammal liable to be seen should be mentioned there whatever its origin. In some instances these importations have spread fast as with the Sika and Barking Deer and the Grey Squirrel, whilst others such as the Fat Dormouse have spread only a few miles in sixty years in spite of a good rate of breeding and successful colonisation. The check-list will show also that although there are a fairly large number of individual species and sub-species, many are closely alike, and some are simply local races of the same creature. Therefore, it is felt unnecessary to describe each one which would lead to much boring repetition when a description of the typical form will suffice to give a fair insight into the animal's ways.

Finally should be mentioned the whales. These may seem remote from what is conventionally accepted as a wild animal, but they are as truly mammals as the rabbits, mice, deer and man. Their breeding ways are identical and their only difference lies in a complete adaptation to aquatic life. They are therefore included not only because they are so often seen from the land but also because they hold a great fascination for all.

ORDER—INSECTIVORA

General Note

The animals of this order are by no means all insectivorous, though there is some reason for the name.

It includes three families: TALPIDAE—Moles; ERINACEIDAE—Hedgehogs, and SORICIDAE —the Shrews. The first two contain only one British example each, but together with the shrew family there are nine British examples of the order.

Several of these shrew species are distinctive island races with marked differences from the typical mainland form. The Jersey Shrew and the Islay Shrew are examples.

They all have much in common. The diet, though varied, is similar and they share a reputation for great voracity and a necessity to be more or less continuously eating. They seem to have a high rate of metabolism and are what would be described, in humans, as ' highly strung.' Being entirely carnivorous they are for the most part beneficial to man in destroying slugs, insect pests and the like, and in this respect differ greatly from the mice they so closely resemble.

Common to the shrews is the scent gland in the flank, secreting an offensive, musk-like smell, which may well be responsible for their flesh being held in no great esteem by the larger carnivorous animals. The shrew is said to have a toxic bite and there are species whose saliva is definitely poisonous, acting much like the venom of an adder.

The life expectancy of a shrew is about 14 to 16 months. This is based on the belief that each animal will go through one breeding cycle and die the following autumn. A young shrew born in May, therefore, would thrive until the next spring, breed then and die in the following autumn or winter.

All the insectivores have a distinction in that the feet are ' platingrade '—a term which implies the heel as well as the toe in contact with the ground. The form of their heads is somewhat alike, having a snout considerably longer than the lower jaw. They all have a close velvety texture to their coats, the pin-cushion hedgehog being a familiar exception.

The Insectivora is a primitive order, there having been little evolution over a great period of time. The brain spaces of its members are small with the accent on their sense of smell.

THE HEDGEHOG

Description

This familiar, short-legged spiny animal, frequently rolling in a ball when disturbed, is unmistakable. The adult male, the ' boar ' is about ten and a half inches long with the ' sow ' an inch shorter, and their tails measure about one and a quarter inches. The weight is about one and a half pounds and both feet and hands are five-toed.

Colour Phases

The general impression is dark brown with the tips

of the quills much lighter or nearly white. The soft fur underneath, which shows as a fringe when the animal is fully uncurled, is a lighter dun colour contrasting sharply with the black feet.

The young ones are much paler with soft spines which gradually stiffen in maturity when the animal becomes a dull grey, finally developing into the adult stage with spines banded light and dark. There is no seasonal colour change.

Habitat

This is a ubiquitous creature that may be seen by night on almost any road, often surprising people with its proximity to houses and towns. Banks, hedges and spinneys or anywhere that will afford it cover in the day, are the hedgehog's home.

Distribution

The typical British Isles race is found all over Western Europe. Its range is flexible, and though in the main a lowland species it is by no means uncommon on high ground.

Habits

A crepuscular and nocturnal animal by habit, the hedgehog may often be seen abroad in daylight after heavy summer rain showers when it seizes the opportunity to hunt slugs which the wet has enticed into the open.

It is the only member of the Insectivora to hibernate for the winter, although it will break off its winter sleep in conditions of unusually fine weather, to hunt around. Unlike the Dormouse it has no food store, a fact that is understandable for a carnivore. The winter and breeding nest is a leaf- and moss-lined hole in a bank, carefully chosen for concealment and protection from the weather.

The hedgehog is a splendid escapist and climber and swims well in emergency. It will climb wire netting without difficulty, and by relaxing its spines, pass through a very narrow opening, facts which are often discovered by boys who seek to keep them for pets. As a rule they respond well in captivity and become very tame, especially the younger ones which are willing and indiscriminate eaters. Like the other Insectivora they are very close-sighted making them easy to watch and to catch in the hand. The only disadvantage of the latter action, beside the obvious, is that they are so verminous. There are no stink glands present in spite of the popular belief.

Food

The hedgehog is as near omnivorous as anything can be, slugs, snails, beetles and worms are the usual fare. It will kill and eat lizards, slow-worms and small snakes and is said to be immune to the venom of the adder. It will kill fair-sized animals and birds when it can overpower them, and is certainly responsible for the final destruction of many injured animals of all kinds. The most unattractive carrion and the eggs of ground-nesting birds are all part of its fare.

Breeding

The boars are extremely quarrelsome throughout the breeding season which lasts from the end of May to the end of August. Boars and sows mate for life. Following a gestation period of about one month, a litter of some four to seven blind and helpless young are born. There are generally two litters in a season, the first being towards the end of May, the pregnancy for the second litter beginning when the young of the first are weaned. By the following year a young hedgehog has reached sexual maturity.

Voice

The most noticeable is a quiet grunt and snuffle as the animal moves about; the young have a high-pitched squeak, and the adults will squeal when picked up or alarmed. It is a noisy eater and can often be heard on a still night, chewing in the dark.

Enemies

The hedgehog has obvious culinary drawbacks which are best overcome by man. Gipsies still eat them in plenty and still employ the age-old method of baking them in clay over an open fire; the meat is excellent. Foxes, badgers and otters will take and eat the hedgehog, rolling it into water to make it uncurl. But its way of poking about the highroads after dark undoubtedly makes the wheels of motor-cars one of its greatest enemies of all.

THE COMMON SHREW

Description

A small velvety animal, some three inches long, with a very long snout and tiny eyes, is the Common Shrew. The colour is red-brown paling to a yellowish-grey underneath. Colour is however most variable in the shrew and the animal can be very dark brown above. A physical characteristic is a gland in the flank emitting an unpleasant musk-like smell which may well be responsible for the unpalatability of these animals for many of their enemies.

Habitat

Generally spread throughout open country and woods alike.

Distribution

The Common Shrew is distributed throughout Europe, including Great Britain, but not Ireland. It is to be found from sea level to a height of about

1,500 feet on the hills. There are very closely allied species isolated on certain islands, as in the case of some of the mice, typical examples being the Islay Shrew and the Jersey Shrew. In both cases there is believed to be sufficient biological difference to make them qualify as separate species.

Habits

This animal seems to be more noticeable in the evening, though it is out both night and day, and feeds at an incessant rate. It is often to be seen running here and there with its long snout reaching up and snapping insects off grass and leaves. It winters in thick and secluded hedges but does not hibernate, although it is frequently suspected of so-doing. Its summers are spent in more open country where it can frequently be seen climbing high in hedges and scaling the stems of tall grasses in search of its food.

The breeding nest is a cup-shaped structure with a loose roof.

Like all shrews it is an extremely pugnacious animal (hence Shakespeare's title, *The Taming of the Shrew*) and it is not infrequent to see fights to the death, particularly in the breeding season.

The animal has a characteristic sleeping attitude with its snout pressed down and protected between the forelegs and the chest.

Food

A very high metabolic rate causes all these animals to be extremely voracious feeders, and the shrew seldom stops eating. Should it be deprived of its supply of food it will be dead in a matter of hours. Insects, snails and wood-lice are its staple diet but its tastes are catholic.

Breeding

The breeding season is May to October, and the

average litter from five to seven, but more have been known in spite of the animal only having six nipples. The second litter is gestated while the first is suckled. There are seldom more than two litters, and the larger litter is always the first one. The period of gestation is about nineteen days, and the period of lactation of similar length. The young will breed in the following year.

Voice

The Common Shrew has a typical range of high-pitched squeaks of which some are inaudible to the human ear.

Enemies

These include hawks and owls, also crows, stoats and weasels, and in certain instances snakes. They appear, however, to share with other members of the family, a certain culinary unpopularity, and it seems that many carnivores which kill them in mistake for voles or mice discard them when they discover their error.

THE PIGMY SHREW

Description

This is the smallest of all British mammals, weighing only five grammes and measuring only some two and a quarter inches head and body. It closely resembles the Common Shrew but has a slightly more hairy tail, which being seven-eighths of the length of the body makes it somewhat longer in proportion. Its colour, though variable, is predominantly brown above with white below, with a fairly hard line of distinction between. It has two moults in the year.

Habitat

The Pigmy Shrew is common throughout fairly wooded districts both in the lowlands and on high ground.

Distribution

This animal is found throughout Europe. Its distribution throughout the British Isles is general,

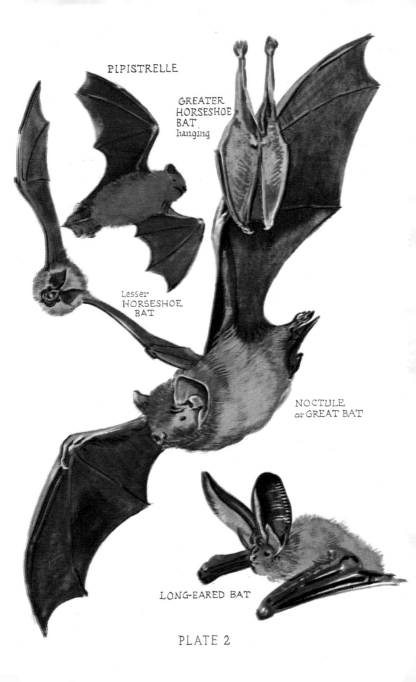

PIPISTRELLE

GREATER
HORSESHOE
BAT
hanging

Lesser
HORSESHOE
BAT

NOCTULE
or GREAT BAT

LONG-EARED BAT

PLATE 2

even including the Outer Hebrides, and it is the only member of the Shrew family to be found in Ireland.

Habits

The Pigmy Shrew does not appear to burrow itself, but generally uses old mouse-holes. Its nest can be found in long grass, holes or tree-stumps, and the material from which the nest is made depends upon what is available in the surroundings. Its nest is similar to that of the Common Shrew, a round hollow ball.

Food

The Pigmy Shrew is a pugnacious little animal and will eat more or less anything that it can overpower. Its staple diet however consists of invertebrates, such as insects, moths and the like.

Breeding

Breeding earlier than the Common Shrew there is a chance for more litters, and though two is the normal, three is not uncommon. The average number in each litter is six, the variation being between two and eight, and the breeding period May to September. Gestation of the new litter commences during the suckling of the previous one, and its period is about nineteen days.

Voice

This Shrew has a tremendous range of high-pitched, needle-sharp cries, many of which lie in so high a pitch as to be inaudible to the human ear; those in the lower are cricket-like and though frequently heard, often mistaken for the sounds of insects.

Enemies

Though the flesh of the shrews seems to be unpalatable to most carnivores, they are killed by them, if only by mistake. They are however definitely eaten by owls in whose pellets a great number of shrew remains are to be found, and also by many of the day-flying hawks; crows, jays and magpies will also eat shrews. These animals are often found dead and untouched, and though known to have a short life it is quite possible that many of them have fallen victim to animals which have refrained from eating them after the kill has been made.

THE WATER SHREW

Description

Although considerably larger than the other shrews, being three to three and a quarter inches long body and head, this animal shares all their characteristics in appearance. It is however somewhat shorter and broader in the snout, and the tail is longer than the body. Colour is as variable as in the other species of shrew, but the upper parts are in the main dark brown or slaty black, with the underparts light grey or whitish, appearing extremely pale by contrast. The feet are brown and broad with a double fringe of hair to act as paddles, for the animal is designed for a water habitat. The underside of the tail is keeled with hair to form a rudder.

Habitat

River banks, ponds, the edges of streams and lakesides are the home of the Water Shrew.

Distribution

Like its relative the Common Shrew, it is spread

all over the United Kingdom, though it is absent from Ireland, the Isle of Man and the Outer Hebrides.

Habits

Like all the Insectivora this animal is very near-sighted and for this reason may be watched for long periods and gives the appearance of great tameness. It is out by day and night. When watched under water it often appears to be covered with silver, due to small particles of air trapped in its coat and carried down with it. The animal dives often and will not infrequently leap out of the water after low-flying insects.

Water Shrews are great fighters, especially the breeding males, and are occasionally known to be gregarious, great migrations along rivers having been observed from time to time. They will often make journeys overland and there are quite a number of known colonies a considerable distance from water, where other conditions seem to be to their liking.

Food

Because of its waterside habits the Water Shrew's diet naturally tends towards aquatic invertebrates, but also includes frogs, newts, molluscs, etc.

WILD CAT

BADGER

FOX

PLATE 3

Breeding

The breeding habits of the Water Shrew follow closely those of the others, the breeding period being May or June and the litter being five to eight which are born blind and naked. These young are, however, independent in five to six weeks, and there is often a second brood in September.

Habitat

Its home is a burrow in a bank, with an inner chamber lined with moss and fine roots to form a round breeding nest.

Voice

The chirrup of the Pigmy Shrew is described as being like that of a cricket, and is equally typical of this animal; it has the same range of high-pitched squeaks as the Common Shrew.

Enemies

Without doubt the owl is the biggest single enemy of this animal, and by virtue of their propensity for diving they will also, from time to time, fall victims to pike and large perch.

THE MOLE

Description

A squat cylindrical body seven or eight inches long with very short legs is the impression one has of a mole. The weight is about six ounces. The head tapers to a pointed snout and both the eyes and the ears are almost impossible to find. The animal is covered with a dark grey velvety fur with no direction to its lay, and this fur was once popular in the well-known rural attire of the moleskin waistcoat. No seasonal colour change is recorded, though tremendous variation is common; frequently moles are caught which are dun in colour or cream, pale grey or pied, and there is often a golden form. Short and immensely powerful hands face outwards and appear to be connected directly to the body, so short are the legs.

Distribution

The species found in Great Britain is distributed throughout Europe as far south as the Mediterranean coast. It is to be found everywhere in the British Isles with the exception of Ireland.

Habitat

The mole is almost entirely subterranean in habit, emerging above ground more frequently in the early spring, probably during the breeding season, and also in conditions of prolonged drought.

Habits

The Mole is the perfect burrowing machine, and evidence of this is its most important field characteristic. An excellent swimmer in times of emergency, it is this very action which it uses to pass through the ground. The four legs are used for scraping backwards and the long snout and strong neck muscles for enlarging the opening ahead. When the Mole has passed a certain distance down its burrow it turns around and forces all the loose earth up and out through one of the vertical shafts, causing the familiar molehill. It is an extremely swift excavator, and when surprised on the surface can disappear in an extraordinarily short time.

Its whole system of tunnels centres itself around the ' fortress,' and there are often several Moles using the same one at the same time.

Food

The Mole has an insatiable appetite like the rest of the Insectivora, and is entirely carnivorous. Earthworms form its staple diet, but it has been known to attack injured birds, and will also kill lizards, small snakes and frogs, and even other Moles that it can overpower.

Its most remarkable feature is its enormous winter store of worms which are kept in the fortress, and have been known to number up to a thousand worms at a time. Close examination has shown that these worms are often damaged at the front end so that although still alive, they are unable to move away, and thus the store can be built up.

Breeding

The boar and sow mate late in March or early in April. Unlike the hedgehog the sow is polyandrous and somewhat independent of the male. She constructs her own nest hill, lining it with a ball of leaves and grass which soon becomes flea-infested. All the nesting material is carried in by the mouth. There is a gestation period of six weeks and the average litter numbers three to four, born blind, naked and pink.

Enemies

The Mole causes more trouble to man than anything else, and therefore man is its chief enemy. Damage to lawns and greens is obvious, but not so obvious is the beneficial effect of the Mole in producing a very effective ground drain. Despite their excellent escape mechanism Moles fall victim to owls, herons, buzzards, and others, and the larger carnivorous animals. When seen working they are often dug out by dogs.

Voice

The Mole has a very loud squeak, especially in alarm.

ORDER—CHIROPTERA

General Note

This order comprises all the bats, which are perfectly normal mammals but endowed with the capability of true flight. Their fore limbs, the bone structure of which corresponds in every way with those of ordinary mammals, are developed with elastic membranes and much elongated fingers; their family name Chiroptera means literally—hand-winged. These wings involve also the structure of the hind legs as well as the tail in all British species. The wing membranes are known to have considerable effect in the location of obstacles and seem to be sensitive to air currents. The ear of the bat is likewise specialised in this way, and it now seems certain that it is employed in the analysis of the echo returns of the bat's own sounds, which give the animal not only a suggestion of what the obstacle might be but an exact location of it. The system is much the same as the echo-sounder used for underwater search, and the special inner ear, or tragus, of most of the bats is probably the principal part of the equipment.

An interesting point is that though bats have a

distinctly audible range of high-pitched squeaks, there is a far greater range of such ultra-sonic transmissions as to be inaudible to the human ear. These are the waves employed by the bat, and there seems to be evidence that they are more or less constantly emitted whilst the animal is on the wing so as to keep it in touch with its immediate sur-roundings by echo. It is this fabulous system which gives the animal its perception and judgment when hunting and makes its flight such a pleasure to watch.

The presence of the ear tragus causes the main division in the bat order. The typical bats belong to

STRUCTURE OF A BAT'S WING

the family VESPERTILIONIDAE and these all have the tragus. They also have a longer tail which, in conjunction with the membranes between the hind feet—the interfemoral membranes—make for a pouch. The remainder, the horseshoe bats, belong to the family RHINOLOPHIDAE. The former are by far the more numerous in Britain, having twelve species, whilst there are only two horseshoe species of bats—the greater and lesser. The names of these two come from the extraordinary nose-leaf formation rather like a horseshoe on the front of the face. This formation of tissue is believed to have an additional sensory property, which may well explain the even greater powers of these particular bats in avoiding obstacles and detecting food.

All British bats are exclusively insectivorous and their whole dentition is planned around this. The insects they take are extremely varied but roughly according to size and capability; hawk moths and stag beetles are by no means safe from the Noctule, whilst the Pipistrelle feeds on much smaller fare. Because they have no free hands they have to catch and handle their food in the mouth, and for this reason bats will sometimes be seen to use the pouch formed by the tail and the hind legs, the after-part of the wing membrane, as a form of grip to manipulate a larger insect so that only its better parts may be eaten and the rest jettisoned. For the most part they feed on the wing, using their unique sense of detection as well as their sight in the hunt. They

24

drink often, and will skim the surface of a pool with great precision not only to lift an insect from its surface, but out of need for water.

The bat's coat is long and silky with little or no lay or direction to it and sharply contrasted with the sleek dark membranes of the wings which are simply an empty hairless sandwich of outer skin layers, stretched over a delicate framework of bone.

The basic structural similarity of bats makes their movements somewhat similar, but in these also the two types, the typical and the horseshoe, show their differences. All of them rest hanging downwards, but whilst the typical bat's wings are gathered in beside him, the horseshoe will wrap itself up completely as in a cloak so that it closely resembles a hanging chrysalis. On the ground, despite their ungainly wings, they can shuffle about quite nimbly, and are able to jump in the air with agility and fly; though they prefer a resting place giving them height enough for a falling start. Their method of alighting is interesting, the typical ones grabbing hold, head uppermost, on a near vertical surface, moving into position afterwards, often deep into some sheltered cranny. The horseshoes on the other hand, with their habit of hanging free from the roof of caves, or similar places, will somersault in the air with the quickest possible movement and come to rest hanging downwards in their chosen place.

While hanging, bats devote much time to grooming, licking the membranes over and sometimes combing themselves with one hind foot whilst hanging with the other; and great are the contortions necessary for much of their toilet. Though carrying their share of fleas and a large wingless parasitical fly peculiar to bats, they seem to bother little about them in their grooming, which suggests that their vermin cause them no great irritation.

Bats are in the main gregarious, often in very large colonies indeed, which in early summer seem to be almost entirely adult females and young of both sexes; while mystery surrounds where the males are at this time in the numbers that would be expected to justify so large a colony of females. Young are born in May to July, and after that the males begin to rejoin in the communal life.

A newly-born bat is naked and it is rare for more than one to be born each year. It is carried about by the mother, clinging to her fur and there are in addition, false teats on the female for the young bat to hold. The period of gestation is in fact about six to seven weeks, though there is great complexity in their sexual behaviour. Pairing takes place in the autumn, with an additional pairing in the following spring, and it is from this second pairing that the young are produced. Bats hibernate after the autumn pairing, a hibernation the complete torpor of which is punctuated by certain periods of movement and activity especially in warm winter weather. It is the comparatively low breeding productivity of bats which may explain their great length of life, for they are long-lived creatures by comparison with the other small mammals, living to an average span of about seven years. The female has her first young when two years old.

By comparison, for example, with the shrews, they are far more restful creatures, crepuscular in habit with much time spent in rest and hibernation, and this may well account for a longer life with much less apparent anxiety and a far lower rate of metabolism.

THE NOCTULE

Description

The largest British bat with short rounded ears, it is
yellowish golden ochre in colour, the velvety fur
extending quite a long way on to the wings. Often
there is rather a rancid smell noticeable when they
are present in quantity. The wing span is between
thirteen and fifteen inches.

Habitat

It colonises holes in trees and buildings and very
seldom in caves. The females form separate summer
breeding colonies, and at this time of the year old
hollow trees are particularly favoured. They are a
very gregarious species, and colonies up to two
hundred are not infrequently found.

Distribution

Noctules are to be found all over the temperate
parts of Europe and Asia. They are common in
the South of England and as far north as a line

drawn from the Tees to the Mersey. North of this line they are extremely rare, and have never been recorded from Ireland.

Feeding and Flight Habits

The flight of the Noctule is powerful and usually rather high up, comprising a straight patrolling passage punctuated by spectacular twists and turns. The larger beetles and moths are its favoured diet.

Flight Time

Noctules appear just before sunset for about one hour, and very rarely as much as two. Occasionally they repeat this flight just before dawn.

Hibernation period

October to end of March.

LEISLER'S BAT

Description

This is very like a scaled-down Noctule, darker brown with considerable summer fading, a slightly paler colour beneath. Its wing span varies between ten and twelve inches.

Habitat

A gregarious animal, favouring holes in trees, buildings and roofs. Though it is frequently met with in a solitary state, it is also found in colonies up to one hundred strong, especially in hibernation during the winter.

Distribution

Leisler's Bat is found right across Europe and Asia. In the British Isles its spread is not completely clear because of confusion with the Noctule. It is known in Eastern Ireland however and the North and West regions of England.

Feeding and Flight Habits

Perhaps because of its relatively short feeding period, it is voracious during that time. Its flight is similar to the Noctule, but generally not at so great a height.

Flight time

Leisler's Bat flies just after sunset for about one hour. It has also a pre-sunrise flight of approximately one hour.

Hibernation period

From the end of September to the end of April.

PIPISTRELLE

Description

This is the smallest of the British bats, and probably the most engaging to watch. Its ears are longer than they are broad and set well apart on the head and the tragus is pointed. The fur on the Pipistrelle is long and extends well on to the wings and to the inter-femoral membranes between the hind legs. Colour varies considerably between dark, light and rufous brown, but the underparts are slightly lighter generally than the upper-parts. Its wing span is about eight to eight and a half inches.

Habitat

The Pipistrelle is often found singly but is also a gregarious bat, the colonies often numbering several hundreds at a time. Normally it is found in crevices in buildings and walls, under bark or under very thick ivy, etc., but it is not generally found in caves.

Distribution

The animal is widely distributed all over temperate

PINE MARTEN

OTTER

PLATE 4

Europe and Asia. It is the commonest British bat and occurs throughout the length and breadth of the land.

Feeding and Flight Habits

This is the bat which is very familiar. Generally it repeats a patrol of set course and length and the same gyrations at each end, and is a familiar sight in country and town alike. It frequently flies in daylight, whether by intention or through disturbance. Its prey is inevitably the smaller insects, for which it uses the tail pouch as a temporary store whilst in flight.

Flight times

From dusk till an hour before the dawn. This length of flight makes it probably the most energetic of all the bats as well as the smallest.

Hibernation period

In the northern part of the British Isles this begins at the end of October and lasts until the end of March, but it is often only partial in the south, and it is by no means an infrequent sight to see the Pipistrelle Bat out in the winter on the milder days.

THE SEROTINE

Description

This is a large bat about the same size as, but a great deal less common than, the Noctule, and it has noticeably broader wings. The ears likewise differ in that they are longer and more oval and spaced rather farther apart. The tragus is long and rounded at the tip. The coat tends to be longer and silkier, and the colour of the animal is dark brown with somewhat lighter underparts. The wing span is between fourteen and fifteen inches.

Habitat

Roofs of houses seem to be the favourite location, and colonies up to twenty are usual.

Distribution

This bat is common in Europe and Asia, but the British Isles is its geographical limit westwards. Not surprisingly, therefore, it is fairly common in Kent, Surrey, Sussex, Hampshire, and the Isle of Wight, and strays farther west into parts of Devon. Everywhere else in the British Isles it is either completely unknown or extremely rare.

Feeding and Flight Habits

The flight is fairly low and seems to be laboured and fluttering; it lacks quite a lot of the zest and aerobatics of the Noctule. Among its favourite diets are cockchafers, but large beetles and large moths are its usual fare. Because of the rarity of the animal there is not a great deal known about its natural history, though considerable study has been devoted to it overseas.

Flight times

The Serotine flies at sunset for about an hour, and as far as is known there is no second flight at sunrise.

Hibernation period

From October to April.

DAUBENTON'S BAT

Description

This is a medium-sized bat with wings comparatively short and broad. The ears are widely spaced, longish and pointed. The tragus is narrow, half the length of the ears and pointed at the tip. The coat is short and a brindled reddish-brown with a distinctly lighter and more yellow colour beneath. Its wing span is about ten inches.

Habitat

Daubenton's Bat is very gregarious. It is a water-loving animal found in woods adjoining water, using caves and trees or ruined buildings and houses anywhere near water. Colonies number up to a hundred or more, sometimes hanging in clusters or wedged into very small crevices.

Distribution

Europe and most of Asia is its range, and it is well-known in England except in the counties of

Gloucestershire, Somerset and Glamorgan, and in the southern part of Scotland.

Feeding and Flight Habits

This bat has a particular liking for water-hatching insects, duns, caddis-flies and the like, and this has led to its name ' Water Bat.' It is a most attractive animal to watch, flying very close to the water and frequently picking insects from the surface.

Flight times

Daubenton's Bat flies all night from one hour after sunset to less than one hour before sunrise.

Hibernation period

It hibernates from the end of September to mid-April, using caves, etc., and hibernating usually singly; the summer roosts are then abandoned.

THE WHISKERED BAT

Description

The Whiskered Bat is small, similar in size to the Pipistrelle. It has long and narrow ears with the tragus over half their length. The coat is long and thick extending on to both surfaces of the wings. Although the lips are fringed with long hairs, it is not unduly whiskered, at least no more so than Daubenton's Bat. The upper surface is dark brown or black with lighter below. Its wing span is about eight and a half inches.

Habitat

In winter it is found hibernating in caves, whilst in summer holes in buildings and roofs are its home.

Distribution

The Whiskered Bat is found across Europe and Asia, and in the British Isles it is generally dispersed from north to south with gaps in South Wales and East Anglia. Though practically missing in Scotland it is fairly common in Ireland. Generally found singly or in very small numbers, it is also gregarious and colonises up to one hundred at a time.

Feeding and Flight Habits

The flight much resembles that of the Pipistrelle but is slower and more staid, and seldom takes in such a wide patrol distance.

Flight times

The Whiskered Bat flies early in the evening, often before sunset, and is believed to fly most of the night. It is also abroad sometimes in the day.

Hibernation period

Extends from November to March, and like the Pipistrelle it is quite frequently found out in daylight or milder winter nights.

NATTERER'S BAT

Description

The Natterer is a medium-sized bat with long narrow ears and a long narrow tragus about two-thirds of their length, pointed at the tip. The coat is long and dark grey or brown above, lighter beneath, with a well-defined border between the two tones. The inter-femoral membrane has a rear border of stiff short hairs which are characteristic of this species and a good mark of identification. Its wing span is about eleven inches.

Habitat

Natterer's Bat hibernates in caves and is gregarious. It is also found in holes in buildings and in trees.

Distribution

Its range extends across Europe and Asia. It is well dispersed about England and Ireland but not in Scotland.

Feeding and Flight Habits

Natterer's Bat has a slow and steady flight generally in the neighbourhood of trees, when it will circle them at a moderate height. If seen from below it will be seen that the tail is carried straight out behind the animal in flight which is a mark of recognition: for other typical bats incline the tail downwards which tends to increase their manoeuvrability. The animal will often be seen to pause in flight to snatch insects which are actually sitting on foliage.

Flight times

Early evening before sunset. The duration of the flight is not exactly known.

Hibernation period

Natterer's Bat is known to emerge from hibernation towards the end of March, but the exact time at which hibernation begins is not accurately known.

THE LONG-EARED BAT

Description

This bat has enormous ears which are clearly seen; their inner edges meet above the head and their outer edges come nearly to the corners of the mouth. The tragus is long and narrow and pointed. In flight the ears are very noticeable and are pointed forward. It is a medium-sized bat with a wing span of about ten inches.

Habitat

This is a gregarious bat forming colonies of fifty to one hundred, in church roofs, eaves, caves, etc. In the summer large colonies of breeding females take up nursing quarters of their own.

Distribution

The Long Eared Bat is spread over Europe and Asia and is very common throughout the British Isles and widely dispersed.

Feeding and Flight Habits

The Long Eared Bat flies close to the ground and swiftly in passage, but when hunting has a gliding flight and will often hover to pick insects off foliage.

Flight times

Half an hour after sunset to one hour before sunrise.

Hibernation period

From mid-October to early April.

THE GREATER
HORSESHOE BAT

Description

This animal is the largest of the leaf-nosed bats and is nearly as big as a Noctule. The wings, however, are very rounded. The ears are large with broad base and sharply pointed tips and there is no tragus. The coat is close and woolly extending on to the wings, and the colour is a reddish-grey with rather lighter underparts. The animal is thirteen to fourteen inches across the wings.

Habitat

Greater Horseshoe Bats are a familiar sight in limestone caves as they hang in hibernation. Summer colonies are to be found in roofs, hollow trees, and similar places, for caves are deserted at that time of year. Like many other bats there is a marked segregation of the sexes.

Distribution

The Greater Horseshoe Bat is spread over Central

Europe and Asia, but in the British Isles is only known in Southern England; it is particularly common in the South West and in South Wales, where its favourite caves are to be found.

Feeding and Flight Habits

This bat has a fluttering flight and its food consists mainly of the larger insects and beetles. Its larger unmanageable catches are pressed into the wing membrane itself during flight, when the animal seeks to manipulate them for greater ease in feeding, there being no tail pouch present in the Horseshoe Bats. Perhaps for this reason it often takes insects up to its roost to eat them at leisure. It is a low-flying bat and often takes flightless insects and spiders off the ground.

Hibernation period

From October till the end of March.

THE LESSER
HORSESHOE BAT

Description

This bat is an exact smaller version of the Greater
Horseshoe Bat, though it is rather greyer in colour
and has a slightly silkier coat. The span of its wings is
about eight and a half inches.

Habitat

Its habitat is very similar to that of the larger
species, the winter colonies being mainly found in
caves.

Distribution

The range is very similar to that of the Greater
Horseshoe Bat; it is found across Europe south of
the Baltic and across southern Asia. It is a common
bat in the South and West of England and in Wales,
but seems to be missing from East Anglia and north
of Yorkshire. It occurs in Ireland, but only in the
West where it is relatively common.

Feeding and Flight Habits

It has a low fluttering flight with intermittent glides and its staple diet are the smaller moths and flies. Having no inter-femoral pouch it uses its inner wing to manipulate its larger catches.

Hibernation period

This extends from October to early April.

ORDER—CARNIVORA

General Note

The CARNIVORA comprise all the beasts of prey, a definition which equally embraces the seals. Two names PINNIPEDIA and FISSIPEDIA classify the two main forms, for the former means fin-footed—the seals, the latter split-footed—the foxes, wild cats, badgers, polecats, and the like. Since their diet gives them their name, it is logical to find that all these animals share the same tooth arrangement and jaw mechanism, a jaw which allows for a deep bite but will not permit the teeth to saw across as in the rabbits and deer. Their brains are large and their intelligence highly developed, as would be expected from animals so closely related to domestic dogs and cats. Scent glands are present in the Carnivora, some to a greater extent than others, and varying in the control exercised over them by the animal concerned. The North American skunk, for example, beats all records with a smell that is itself a guaranteed protection against all comers; the British polecat, and the ferret that has evolved from it, are none too pleasant, and the whereabouts of fox can often be detected without the help of a pack of

STOAT
(Summer Coat)

POLECAT

WEASEL

ERMINE
(Stoat in white
Winter coat)

PLATE 5

hounds. This secretion smell has its own uses, one of which may well be to assist in finding each other, for the carnivores are in the main solitary creatures outside the breeding season. The scent glands are located beneath the tail to either side of the vent.

Another point of interest is that the smallest of the Carnivora are the commonest, a fact that bears through the whole sequence of the extinction of lions, bears and wolves from these islands, leaving the fox the largest land member of the family. Were it not for the rather fortuitous preservation of this animal by the hunts it too might be extinct, for the hand of man is largely set against it. The main forces for the destruction of this family have been brought about by their predatory ways on the one hand and their excellent coats on the other, for all our domestic Carnivora are 'fur-bearers' in the furrier's sense of the word. The condition of their coats is further helped by a strong affinity for grooming common to them all.

As a family they all share a great propensity for play, which is very noticeable in the stoats and the badgers and the otters, and by no means confined to the young alone. It is a form of family exhibitionism and has also an educational sense and a hunting application.

The young of these animals are all born blind and helpless and are therefore raised in considerable seclusion, usually underground. The coat of the young differs in texture from the adult, as does the puppy coat in a dog; and their family life is of a more human and advanced character than most other mammals. The young generally stay long with their parents and are educated by practical demonstration of hunting technique, a frequently-seen example of this being the presentation by the parent of an injured animal or bird for the young to catch and kill.

None of our British Carnivora hibernate for the winter, and many provide a fine study for tracking in the snow; the well-known slides of the otter and the hunting tracks of the stoat betraying much of their ways at this time of the year.

The two sexes in most of them show considerable difference in size, with the males larger than the females. Though this is not too pronounced in the bigger examples, it is most noticeable in the weasels and stoats, and this makes size alone a poor difference to rely upon in telling these two apart.

The cunning, strength and pugnacity of the Carnivora leave few enemies for them except man himself. The gamekeeper looks with disfavour upon most of the members of this tribe, and while the fox enjoys a certain artificial protection in hunting country, it is given very little quarter elsewhere. Perhaps the weasel, the smallest of all, is the only one that falls victim to other predators, and is small enough to be taken fairly regularly by hawks and by the larger owls.

THE FOX

Description

The well-known fox needs little description. It is a large animal twenty-three to thirty-three inches long in the body with a brush twelve to eighteen inches, and weighing between fifteen and twenty-five pounds. Colour varies considerably, but is generally red or yellowish-brown with greyish-white beneath, and a suffusion of greyish-white over the longer coat of the hind quarters. There is generally a white tip to the brush. The feet and the lower parts of the legs are black and likewise the back part of the ears. The dark and light facial markings tend to give it the impression of wearing a grin.

Distribution

The fox is common throughout Europe and Great Britain, though it is absent from the Scottish Islands except the Isle of Skye. Its great natural stronghold is in Wales, and it is an indigenous animal having been in this country since prehistoric times, surviving the extinction of the wolf.

Habitat

Its choice of habitat is unrestricted, and it is to be found from the Highlands to the Fens, often wandering great distances and lying up in woods and scrubland.

Habits

Natural cunning has kept up the numbers of foxes in this country as well as protection and natural inaccessibility. The lair of the fox is usually an enlarged rabbit hole or discarded badger set, known as the ' earth.' In hill country, however, foxes frequently use caves and fissures in the rock. It has a mainly nocturnal habit and lies up during the day, leading a solitary life except in the breeding season. Its gait is an easy lope and its ways wholly dog-like, cocking its leg against vantage points to proclaim its territory, as a dog will treat a lamp-post.

Foxes spend much time in family play and education of the cubs. They have in common with stoats a form of hunting trickery, used particularly for taking rabbits. This involves a frivolous exhibition of leaps and bounds and tail-chasing which has the effect of causing rabbits to cluster round in wonderment, forgetting the danger, until the fox is close enough to take a pounce and secure his prey.

Food

These animals are almost entirely carnivorous, with rabbits topping the list, though recent myxomatosis and the attendant shortage of rabbits has caused a greater diversity of diet. Mice, voles, birds of all kinds are taken, whilst in sheep-country foxes are a great scourge for the toll they take of young lambs. They will raid farmhouses whenever opportunity permits, and have the habit of littering the area around their ' earth ' with the remains of their plunder. It is too early as yet to assess on balance the difference to the numbers of *all* animals which the spread of myxomatosis must have made.

Breeding

Dog and vixen mate once a year, usually in January, and the gestation period is just under two months, cubs being born in March or April, and the general litter about five or six. The dog fox is monogamous and very faithful indeed, seldom mating another vixen should the first be killed. The period of lactation is eight to ten weeks and the eyes of the cubs are open after ten days; they are fully grown in six months.

Voice

The vixen in the breeding season has a wailing call

which is a familiar sound in coverts at night. The reply of the dog is a short bark, both sounds being very dog-like in character.

THE BADGER

Description

The badger is a large shuffling animal, the distinctive markings of which are far better shown by the drawing than described. The main body-colour suggests, reasonably enough, the old-fashioned shaving brush which was made from their coat; and the coat of the young closely resembles that of the parents. Badgers will weigh between twenty and thirty pounds, while individual animals have been known to reach over forty pounds. Their body length averages between twenty-four and thirty inches with a short, six-inch tail.

Distribution

Badgers are firmly though unobtrusively entrenched throughout England and Wales but are infrequent in East Anglia and less common in Scotland. In Ireland it is well-known and in remote areas of that country is still eaten by man in the form of badger hams.

Habitat

The badger moves abroad considerable distances at night but favours for the site of its set a woodland location, generally in a steep bank.

Habits

Though nocturnal and very unobtrusive, this animal is prepared to live near man and seems to have no essential fear of him. Badgers are great diggers and often live in the same set for generation after generation, enlarging it with their different families until a tremendous earthworks has been formed.

Their nightly duties are a great pleasure to watch. On emerging from the set one of the first actions is usually a prolonged and vigorous scratching of the coat using claws rather than the tongue for grooming the long hair and shaking it into place rather in the fashion of a dog. They will frequently bring out their bedding to air it and spend much time in play and the education of their young.

Their sets are easily distinguishable from those of a fox by the remains of bedding that lie about and usually by the great mass of moved earth; although foxes are frequently tenants of the larger badger sets they seldom do so much digging. Nearby there will frequently be found trees barked with vertical scratches where these animals have stretched up to sharpen their claws. The badger is strikingly different from the fox in points of sanitation, even to the extent of digging a latrine trench and never fouling the set.

Food

The badger does not force itself on man's attention as does the fox, and although the occasional rogue badger will raid a farmhouse it is generally more discreet about it and does not litter the area with pieces of poultry. It has an extraordinarily wide and almost omnivorous diet, which includes a considerable vegetable content. It will eat acorns, wild bulbs, nuts and roots, and apples; it rootles about in the fashion of a pig, taking slugs, worms and beetles, and will turn over wasps' nests for the grubs. It will take rabbits and the smaller mammals and birds when it can, but for the most part it will go for the injured ones. Hedgehogs on the other hand fall frequently prey to a badger because of their slow movements, and a badger will skin them to rid them of their spines.

Breeding

The sexes are referred to as boar and sow and mate in mid-July to August. Their system of reproduction is, however, extremely unusual and most interesting in that there is a suspended stage in the development of a fertile cell, and this is known as delayed implantation. The true gestation period lasts only about eight weeks and the litters are born early in March to late April. These young are sometimes called earth-pigs, and the litter generally numbers three to four.

Voice

From time to time badgers will emit a blood-curdling shriek, the necessity for which is not established, but it is known to have little courting significance. The fine repertoire of snufflings made by the animal about its feeding are quiet and can only be heard when close at hand.

THE OTTER

Description

From twenty-five to thirty-two inches long, with sixteen to eighteen inches of tail or rudder, and weighing anything from fifteen to thirty-five pounds, the otter is unmistakable by its characteristic shape and water habitat. Liver brown and close-coated above with greyish-white underparts, it is a powerful sleek animal with a long tail, thick at the base, short legs and webbed feet. The head is curiously flat, and the jaws strongly whiskered; the eyes are like black boot-buttons.

Distribution

This is a European species spread well through Britain, occurring on many rivers and Highland lochs and extending well into estuaries and open rocky coasts. Though it is seldom seen because of its retiring ways, it is probably far more numerous than one would tend to believe.

Habits

Though largely nocturnal the otter is by no means hard to find by day. It is a playful animal delighting to toy with the fish it catches with such ease and grace, and so often discards without eating. The stronghold or holt is typically the holes beneath tangled alder roots and the like, often with the only entrance under water. In parts of the Norfolk Broads, however, where they tend to be rather more numerous, the holt is often an open-topped nest in the vast reed-beds.

It has a clear rather flute-like whistle which is often to be heard around dusk to herald the beginning of the evening's hunt. Its swimming motion is both graceful and powerful, using the tail as a stern oar, whilst the underwater track is discernible by fine bubbles on the surface.

The playfulness of these animals is frequently reflected in the characteristic slides which they make of hard-baked earth to glissade into the water. In hard weather similar slides are made in the snow.

Food

Though predominantly a fish-eater, and a somewhat wasteful one in that it discards a great many of its catches, it will also take reptiles and water mammals with occasional sorties ashore after different fare. Coastal otters will also take small crusaceans.

Breeding

There seems to be no fixed breeding season for the otter and study is made extremely difficult by the inaccessibility of the animal, with the result that the predominance of its breeding habits are still unknown. Litters however number generally two or three and are born during the winter, to remain in the parents' company around the holt until nearly full grown and their hunting education complete.

THE PINE MARTEN

Description

The Pine Marten is an active, arboreal animal, some sixteen to twenty-three inches long with a good foot of bushy tail; its weight is about three pounds. It is richly dark brown in colour with a most striking yellowish patch on the chest.

Distribution and Habitat

This is essentially a woodland animal and is found throughout Europe and Asia and as far north as the tree-line. In the United Kingdom its extreme rarity and near extinction is a tragedy, though it is still to be found in the remoter parts of the Scottish Highlands in dense fir woods and in the Lake District, Wales and Ireland.

Habits

This animal used to be called Sweet Marten because its secretions from the stink glands are a great deal less unpleasant than that of the polecat. To-day it is sometimes called the Marten Cat. It leads an arboreal life not unlike that of a squirrel, and its long claws are ideally developed for it.

For a summer nest it will often reline an old squirrel's drey or the discarded nest of a crow; it will equally often take to the ground, nesting as a polecat does, using a rock crevice or tree-root hole.

Food

The Pine Marten is adept at catching squirrels, but also has a vegetarian content to its diet for it eats highland berries, and birds and their eggs, and bearlike will rob the honey from wild bees.

Breeding

The great rarity of this animal makes observation difficult. It is believed to experience delayed implantation. In the case of the similar animal from America, however, mating is July to August and the young are born the following spring, the litter numbering four to five. It may also raise two litters a year.

THE STOAT

Description

The Stoat is a slim, active, lithe little animal nine to twelve inches long with a four and a half inch tail. It is reddish-brown above and yellowish beneath with a noticeable black tip to the tail. The male is considerably larger than the female. Like the weasel it has two moults per year, but in the northern area where snow persists, the winter coat is a white one retaining only the black tail tag. There are however cases of a partial moult only, usually leaving patches of brown about the head. The white winter change is extremely rare in Ireland. This colour change takes place rapidly due to the white coat having grown almost to maturity beneath the old one before moulting begins.

Distribution

A typical form of the stoat exists all over Europe, including all the British Isles, and its habitat is quite general being both a highland and lowland species and an animal which casual observers

COMMON SEAL and PUP

GREY SEAL and PUP

PLATE 6

frequently see crossing roads at night and even in the daytime. Like the rest of the Carnivores it travels far.

Habits

The Stoat is a great hedgerow hunter by night but is far less nocturnal in habit than any of the other Carnivores and is frequently out by day. Not uncommonly the stoat hunts in packs of considerable size and utters while doing so a shrill yikkering cry. They are apt in this manner to have large overland migrations in considerable quantities, and such movements of the stoats have been reported from all parts of the country. Such a large-scale movement can easily be a considerable danger to anyone in their path, due to the great ferocity of the little animals. The terror inflicted by the stoat upon the rabbit and even the hare, by what appears to be a form of fear hypnosis is well-known, the prey becoming almost paralytic with fright and easy to take.

The stoat's usual breeding nest is a hole in a tree or the premises of an evicted mole.

Food

The stoat is a voracious Carnivore, eating any animal or bird that it can overpower and forcing its attention upon man as a real enemy of the poultry farmer. Its cunning and slimness will gain it access to the most carefully protected runs. The stoat falls foul of the gamekeeper for its depredations to all game.

Breeding

Stoats mate soon after their breeding, the young

STOAT IN WINTER

being born in April; but like the badger they go through delayed implantation, and though the gestation period is in fact no more than about one month, there can be a space of nine or ten months between actual mating and the birth of the litter.

Young female stoats reach maturity at a surprisingly early age, two months only, and mate the same summer as that in which they are born. The male as well as the female has a period of fertility; the male stoat is potent only between the months of March and July. The number of a typical litter is four or five.

THE WEASEL

Description

An extremely agile, slim, snake-like little animal is the weasel, very short on the leg and measuring six to eight inches long with a short two to three inch tail which lacks the black tip of the stoat. Weasels have no white coat in Britain, persisting throughout the year with the reddish-brown pattern similar to that of the stoat, though the yellow or white under-parts of the weasel are rather sharper and more clearly defined. Again the difference in size between the male and female is very marked, the male being considerably larger.

Distribution and Habitat

These animals are general throughout Britain in highlands and lowlands alike, their habitat corresponding more or less exactly with that of the stoat.

Habits

Though chiefly nocturnal the weasel is active by day

and a most bloodthirsty little animal, acutely pugnacious. It will often climb into hedges and low trees after nests and young birds and displays the stoat's technique of charming its prey by a wild display of antics, intriguing the prey off its guard until it can be taken unawares.

Food

The weasel takes rats, mice, moles, frogs, small birds and poultry. Its diet is however very much more confined to mice than any of the other Carnivores. It should not be regarded therefore to be the same threat as the stoat to the interests of man; it can, in fact, be said to share some of the benefits of the owl in this respect. It is a strong swimmer and will even catch the water vole in its own element.

Breeding

There is no delayed implantation as in the stoat. Two litters are raised annually, numbering usually five. Breeding is from March to August, mating for the second litter beginning soon after the first litter is born, and gestation is believed to be about six weeks. The male weasel is infertile throughout the winter.

THE POLECAT

Description

Like the badger, the rather intricate patterning of
the polecat is easier to illustrate than describe. Its
main coat is of a subtle texture and colour caused by
the mixture of a dark upper and light undercoat.
Polecats weigh from one and a half to two and a
half pounds and measure about fifteen to seventeen
inches in the body with a six-inch tail.

Distribution

Polecats are distributed all over Europe with an
allied form in Asia. In Great Britain however
persistent trapping has driven them out of nearly
every county to their final stronghold in central
Wales where they are still able to survive. This has
happened within the last hundred years.

Habitat

Woods and copses and secluded river valleys and
their attendant marshes are the home of the polecat.
Their lair will be made in rock holes, tree roots and
wood piles.

Habits

The ancients called this animal Foul Marten because of its stink glands, a quality which has brought ' polecat ' into the language as a simile for the odorous. It is a smell well-known to all those who keep ferrets, the domesticated counterpart.

Polecats are rapacious and hunt by night, tending often to kill more than they can eat. They will raid hen-houses and are perfectly prepared to kill turkeys and geese. Their ways and habits follow very closely those of the stoat; it has somewhat the same tendency to hunt in small packs and indulges in the same play as the other Carnivores which it so closely resembles.

Food

The staple diet of the polecat is rabbits, though it takes birds and smaller rodents. In one of its favourite marsh habitats it has a strong craving for frogs and will take eels from the water.

Breeding

The polecat is believed to raise only one litter a year which numbers five or six, after a gestation period of about forty days. The pairing takes place in February with the young born in April or May.

THE WILD CAT

Description

The wild cat is surprisingly like a large domesticated tabby but with a much fiercer demeanour, flattened ears, and a shorter stiffer tail. Its length is twenty to twenty-five inches with a tail about eleven to fourteen inches; its weight is somewhere between seven and fourteen pounds. Its general colour is a very variable tabby-grey, somewhat barred, and having a ringed dark and light tail. There is undoubtedly a good deal of interbreeding with semi-wild domestic cats, and this has altered not only the habits but also in some ways the appearance of the truly wild species.

Distribution

This is a European and Northern Asiatic species which has in these islands been confined now to the far mountain fastnesses of Scotland particularly in the counties of Ross, Perth, Inverness and Sutherland.

It is altogether missing in Ireland.

Habitat

It is to be found in the remotest parts of rock-strewn hills and highland woods, coming occasionally into the glens to lie up in dense reeds. The breeding nest will be a rock cleft or the bole of a hollow tree.

Habits

Some say that this animal for its size is the fiercest in the world. It can be best described in habit by comparing it to the wildest domestic cat and adding a wide margin. Its night cries are the same but far wilder and more harsh. Its techniques of hunting vary little from the typical farm cat, though its disposition is that of a tiger.

Food

Rabbits are certainly foremost in its diet but it takes birds and mice and undoubtedly its share of Highland game—a wage that it should be gladly allowed for its rarity.

Breeding

In the true species there is said to be only one litter each year, which is born in early summer and numbers four or five kittens. In the Scottish form however there is displayed the effects of inter-breeding with a domestic strain and there are generally two litters, one in May and another in August. Not infrequently there is a third winter litter born. Even the kittens display a fierceness which is seldom lost even in captivity.

THE SEALS

General Note

Another division of the order CARNIVORA are the seals—PINNIPEDIA, and there are two well-established British species, the Atlantic Grey Seal and the Common Seal. They are animals fully adapted for a marine life, being quite ungainly on land, and they should not be confused with the Sea Lions of circuses which are more developed for a compromise existence between land and water. These latter animals are of a tropical species unknown to our waters.

Despite the unusual and specialised shape of the seal it is still a true mammal; and though there are no legs as such, the whole corresponding bone system is present beneath the skin, the tail flippers having the same parts as the legs, feet and toes of the normal mammal though by comparison greatly more restricted in movement. On land the seal can move over a short distance with surprising agility, using much the method of progression one sees in a grub or caterpillar, a hitching up of the back and thrusting of the tail flippers. The Common Seal will use the hand flippers too for movement on sand, and seldom lies unprotected far from the water, being conscious of its vulnerability if surprised.

Anyone who has had the luck to watch seals about their business will know of their prowess in the water. Despite their great wariness they are playful inquisitive creatures and will often come towards a boat to investigate, particularly if there is a source of music on board. Seals seem to use all their senses in the pursuit of fish, frequently swimming on their backs in clear water the better to survey the bottom for flat fish. In thick water however they must employ a tactile sense as the otter does with its well-developed whiskers, little else could explain the fishing success of the Common Seals of the East Coast in the thick mud of their estuaries. The ears are but small holes, closed under water, but there must be employment for them also in the hunt. In diving the seal is endowed with the capability of holding its breath for a surprising period; this is known to attain twenty minutes in the case of the Grey Seal and slightly less for the Common one. Both species will regularly stay submerged for five to eight minutes while fishing.

Colour of seals varies enormously, and variation is further intensified by their tones altering in colour with the wetness of their coats. The young of both species are born white or yellowish; but in the case of the Common Seal this puppy coat is shed extremely early and at times even before birth. Both species follow their puppy coat with a blue-grey yearling coat which lasts for some twelve months before the adult coat grows in.

The only enemy of seals is man, and in rare cases the Killer-Whale, and this is noticeable in their choice of habitat, a choice which is also influenced by their breeding habits and by the fact that the Common Seal pup is a great deal more independent young animal than that of the Grey Seal. This will be further described in the habitat of the two species. They tend to be gregarious animals especially at breeding times, whilst between times they will spread about singly.

Their food is in the main fish, though there is little information available on exactly what types and how far they are in fact a nuisance to fishermen, despite the popular belief to that effect. It can be assumed, however, that the Common Seal living in shallow East Coast waters is certainly more likely to be a serious competitor in this respect, although its diet is known to contain fair quantities of molluscs as well as marketable fish.

It should be mentioned that there are several Arctic species of seals whose occurrence has been recorded and a repetition of their appearance is always possible. Although their rarity makes it unnecessary to describe them in detail they should be mentioned. There is the little five-foot Harp Seal and Ringed Seal and the larger Hooded Seal, and the very large Bearded Seal which can measure twelve feet and weigh half a ton.

THE COMMON SEAL

Description

The Common Seal is noticeably smaller than the
Grey one, measuring some six to eight feet, and
though variation is very great it is generally a

rather browner or warmer colour and has a more dog-like and less Roman-nosed profiile than the Grey Seal. A better and far more certain guide however to rough identification than any other is that of habitat.

Habitat and Distribution

The Common Seal definitely favours the estuarine and sandy type of habitat and is therefore the common seal of the East Coast, the Wash, and is only very occasionally found on the rockier West Coast. Outside Britain its range extends right up the East Atlantic Coast from Spain through Scandinavia and round by the north west Atlantic coast as far south as New England.

Habits

In the normal way of things a seal is little more than a flat head with big dark eyes on the surface of the water. They may however be better seen on East Coast sandbanks where very large gatherings can sometimes be seen; and under these conditions where the clearness of water permits they may be very easily observed from the air swimming under water. Persecution has made the Common Seal an extremely wary animal and they will seldom lie-up in places where they can be easily approached or surprised.

Breeding

The young of the Common Seal are born in June
and July and are able to swim within hours of their
birth. It is therefore possible for a pup to be born
on the sandbanks at low water and floated off by
the next flood tide, being fully able to cope with the
situation. It seems that the pup is not suckled in the
water and feeds are therefore confined to occasions
when the mother and pup can come ashore. Her
milk however is extremely rich and the pup grows
at a tremendous rate.

Food

Difficulty of study makes it impossible to be certain
which fish constitute the main diet of the Common
Seal. They can however often be seen eating flat
fish and are known to take salmon and sea trout,
and undoubtedly the other migratory fish, mackerel,
and the like which come into these waters in the
warmer months. The Common Seal is however
known to take a very fair quantity of molluscs in its
diet, and is estimated to consume approximately
ten pounds of food in a day.

RED
DEER

FALLOW
DEER

MUNTJAC
or
BARKING
DEER

ROE
DEER

PLATE 7

THE GREY SEAL

Description

This animal is considerably the larger of our two seals, the bulls weighing up to six or seven hundred-weight. It is a darker animal upon which black spots are generally so close together or so large as to give it a much blacker appearance than the Common Seal, and the profile of the bull is definitely Roman-nosed with a convex rather than a concave brow. The length varies between eight and eleven feet, with the bull much larger than the cow; but like the Common Seal considerable certainty of identification is much easier from the habitat than from any other single point.

Habitat and Distribution

The breeding habits of the Grey Seal are such that it favours a rocky coast and is therefore predominant in the South West and up to the Hebrides and is extremely uncommon on the East Coast. Its Atlantic range extends from Nova Scotia right round the North Atlantic to the Baltic Sea.

Habits

It is logical that these two headings should be put together as the only time which this animal really spends ashore is at the breeding period, and it is only then that it can be properly studied. At this period it is gregarious and forsakes the somewhat solitary habit which it enjoys most of the year. The pre-breeding assembly of sexes begins towards the end of summer when cows come ashore prior to bearing their young. One pup only is born, twins being rare. At about this time bulls come ashore in an extremely fat condition after ten months feeding in the sea. The young are born in September and October and are helpless for several days. It is this single aspect which has largely chosen the habitat of the Grey Seal, for it requires a place where the young can be brought well clear of the tide line and looked after in comparative seclusion and suckled until ready for the sea. The mother seal will find a protective cove or sea cave in which the young can be born. At birth the pup will measure about three and a half feet and weigh some thirty pounds, but grows at a tremendous rate due to the extreme richness of the milk. Within three weeks the baby coat has moulted out and large layers of blubber begin to grow under the skin. Directly it is weaned the pup is discarded by its parents, which will be in about four weeks, and the young will not breed in their turn until about four years old. The care which the mother seal bestows upon the pup is sharply in contrast with the bull's indifference, for she will protect the pup vigorously and shield it from gales and from the sun.

The cows are served by the bull very soon after the birth of their young, and by the time the bull has worked himself through his harem his condition has fallen off drastically compared with what it was when he first emerged from the sea. By the time he returns to the ocean after some two months ashore he has declined enormously, has lost a great amount of weight and suffers badly from bleary eyes and halitosis.

Voice

Grey Seals have a repertoire of strange uncanny sounds, many of which have given inspiration to Hebridean folk songs. The pups have a shrill yap uttered continuously around breeding colonies, which themselves are sources of great noise and clamour as cows protect their territories and drive off all interlopers.

ORDER—UNGULATA

THE DEER

General Note

Because the habits and characteristics of the deer are all so much alike it is possible to put far more in this general note than is necessary under each specific species. Only two species of deer remain in Britain from the original indigenous stock and these are the Red Deer and the Roe. There are however a number of semi-wild deer, escapes and import- ations, now freely breeding which must be mentioned for they are likely to be met with in the field. Some need only be mentioned by name, whilst others like the Fallow Deer, the importation of which is believed to have been made by the Romans is well spread throughout the land and worthy of very special note.

All British deer bear horns or antlers which are grown and shed every year. Only the male bears them except in the case of the Reindeer, a species which has been recently brought experimentally into the Highlands. In the case of this animal both sexes have horns.

The growth of the new antlers begins early in the year and as they grow they are covered with a soft furry skin aptly called ' velvet,' which when the horn is fully grown towards the end of the summer finally shreds off in strips to leave the clean horn exposed. After this point the antlers are fully hard and ossified and will grow no more; whilst in velvet however they are relatively soft and vulnerable, bleeding easily if damaged.

Deer are ruminants, they chew the cud, and the stomach arrangement is therefore the same as that of a cow. They are entirely herbivorous browsing animals with the added habit of chewing their own cast antlers as being the easiest method of re-assimilating the calcium needed for the new growth. Experiments have shown that where artificial calcium salts have been provided for them the tendency to chew the antlers is not so marked.

The deer tribe rely upon their swiftness for survival; whilst hand in hand with this go extremely well-developed sight, hearing and smell, the organs of which are ever active, keeping the animals constantly on the alert.

It will be possible to mention much more of the biology of the deer in the chapter on the Red Deer; whilst the illustrations will have to suffice to show some of the physical points of the imported species.

Principal among these recent importations are the beautiful Sika from Japan and Manchuria, a dark animal with a fine six to eight-point head.

MUNTJAC BUCK

SIKA BUCK

There is the Chinese and Indian Muntjac or Barking Deer, the Siberian Roe and the Chinese Water Deer. The habits of all these run closely with those which will be described, and many of them are gaining firm footholds in this country in areas of re-afforestation.

Finally should be mentioned the other ungulates, the semi-feral goat which exists in parts of Wales and in the Scottish Islands, and also the Soay Sheep of the St. Kilda group. These however run so close to the domestic animal there is little point in mentioning them more than by name.

THE RED DEER

Description

This is the largest of the British deer averaging about four feet high at the shoulder. It is a magnificent animal, dark reddish-brown above with a dark line along the backbone and down the back of the flanks throwing into relief the light ' speculum,' a patch on the buttocks, which is pale buff. The underside is lighter. The stags, especially in the autumn breeding season or ' rut,' grow a thick mane on the neck. The calf is dappled with white in its early coat, being mature in colour after eight weeks.

When the animals are well nourished, Red Deers' antlers, dark but white-tipped, increase in size, weight and number of points each year until they reach their prime, after which the animal will decline, or ' go back ' as it is called, the horn becoming thinner. This is understandable when one considers the natural resources called for in such an annual growth. Every stag has its own head, and there is no set pattern in the Red Deer, though there is a certain trend towards similarity, and there is an approximate formula to which the tines comply. The growth is generally complete by July each year and the stag in its sixth year is usually at the prime of its growth. If it should have twelve points in all, and these points big enough to hang a hat on, it is a ' Royal.' The perfect textbook ' Royal ' head will comprise two-brow tines which extend forwards over the eyes, a ' bay ' and ' tray ' which extend outwards, and a ' cup ' of three points on the tip of each antler.

Horn-growth is controlled to some extent by conditions of diet and the health of the animal, and freakish heads are therefore not uncommon, including such variations as ' hummel,' that is, a completely hornless stag, or a ' switch,' a beast with brow tines only with a sweep of uninterrupted horn. The ' switch ' head results in a rather danger-ous arrangement which will not lock with the head of another in combat and may therefore cause death to a better beast.

Distribution and Habitat

The Red Deer extends all over Europe, the largest specimens of all coming from East Germany. In these islands its main strength is confined to the Highlands and Islands of Scotland, and the Lakes, and to Exmoor, and to parts of Ireland. Its presence in fair quantity is due chiefly to the protection it is afforded as a beast of the chase, both for stalking in the North and hunting in the South West. Its range however in other isolated places, largely due to the spread of re-afforestation, has increased quite considerably.

Habits and Breeding

The Red Deer is a gregarious animal with a migratory tendency from the higher ground in summer to the lower ground in winter. Except during the rut, from late August or September to early October, the sexes tend to keep apart in stag and hind herds, the latter containing young stags as well up to their third year—' wee knobbers ' as they are called in Scotland. When antlers are clean the rut begins and a great change comes over the community. The formerly silent stag roars a stirring challenge across the glens, and each begins rounding up his own harems of hinds. The ensuing week or two when the stag serves his hinds is punctuated by occasional sorties on his part to drive off would-be challengers; otherwise he spends much of his time lying down to recover his strength and relying upon the watchfulness of his harem to bark their alarm at danger's approach. Rutting lasts about six weeks, usually starting late September, at the end of which the big stags holding harems are worked out and their harems often broken up by smaller beasts.

Calves are dropped in June, one per hind, twins being extremely uncommon. The young calf is able to stand almost immediately after birth and lactation lasts about eight months. Hinds with no calves are known as 'yeld' hinds. The hind generally drops her first calf at the end of her third year. A stag of the same age is sexually mature but not big and strong enough to hold a harem of his own, and relies upon what he can pick up towards the rut's end.

The combat is a classic sight and has been illustrated too often for description to be necessary. It is a fair test of strength, usually between well-matched beasts, and smaller ones knowing their limitations will seldom push a challenge to the length of a real show-down. Seldom are there fatalities, though injury is not infrequent. The normal life-span of the Red Deer is about fifteen years.

THE ROE DEER

Description

The Roe Deer is a small, dainty, red-brown animal with short, sharp, vertical horns generally bearing six points ; and a white ' speculum.' The face is rather darker than the body and there are two white patches on the throat. There appears to be no tail although the vertebral structure for it is there present. Fawns are spotted with white in their first year.

Habitat and Distribution

The Roe Deer is present right across Europe and Asia. In Britain it is well established, tending to increase with re-afforestation: it is much more numerous in the North.

Habits

This is not a gregarious animal like the Red Deer and is mainly nocturnal in habit, lying up in the daytime. They generally move abroad in a family party which would consist of a buck and doe and two fawns, the buck dominating the scene. The bucks have a reputation for considerable pugnacity and there are frequently very spirited fights indeed between them. An interesting characteristic of the Roe Deer are the racing rings, the well-worn tracks made by these animals round bushes and the like and sometimes of most intricate shape. These rings are used in their courtship chases and are a common sight where Roe Deer abound.

Breeding

Twin fawns are the normal progeny for the Roe doe. They are born in May and in considerable seclusion and they are kept there for ten days or so when the party rejoins the buck and stays with him until after the rut in July or August. The mating call of the Roe buck is a characteristic bark, and the doe replies with a far-carrying squeal. This latter call is used to a considerable extent on the continent as a decoy by hunters. Following the rut, bucks tend to take off alone, generally going up to higher ground. By Christmas time they have shed their antlers, and the new growth is complete and clean by the late spring of the following year. In proportion the antlers are not nearly the size of those of the Red or Fallow Deer, and the pattern tends to be very much more regular.

The Roe Deer, like the Badger, goes through delayed implantation, the period between the rut and the birth of the fawn being about nine months, while the embryo is only developing for the last four months of it.

THE FALLOW DEER

Description

The Fallow is an extremely beautiful deer standing about three feet at the shoulder, and in summer is a reddish-fawn colour richly mottled with white. Like the Red Deer, a black line follows the spine and bifurcates around the white speculum. The bucks have relatively very large antlers palmated at the top into wide flat plates. The winter coat is a drab greyish shade with no white spots. The fawns are coloured similarly to their parents.

Distribution and Habitat

The Fallow Deer is a woodland species spread over Europe, and believed to have been introduced into Britain by the Romans. It is a very familiar sight in public deer parks and is widely distributed in open country as a wild and semi-feral species, often many areas causing a considerable amount of damage to crops.

Habits and Breeding

Although park Fallow Deer are gregarious this is

not so to such an extent in the wild state. Bucks gather up their harems in the autumn, the rut beginning in October. Bucks and does remain in company for the rest of the year, but during the summer until the next rut the bucks remain apart, their antlers being clean by August. The old antlers are not dropped until May. The fawns are born in June.

RABBIT

BLUE HARE
(White Winter
Coat)

BROWN
HARE

PLATE 8

ORDER—LAGOMORPHA

RABBITS AND HARES

General Note

This order was originally included with all the rodents (rats and mice) under the name RODENTIA and has only recently been separated because of biological differences between them, principally in the teeth. The most interesting of these is that the teeth of hares and rabbits are continually growing in life and rely upon regular use and grinding upon their opposite numbers to maintain a reasonable length. It is by no means rare for a tooth whose opposite number has been damaged or lost to grow into freakish proportions, often destroying the animal by making it impossible for it to feed, or even by growing back into the skull itself and damaging the eye or the brain. There is a noticeably large gap between the incisor teeth and the molars and this gap can be closed by the cheeks to give the effect of the incisors working outside the mouth. Rabbits and hares therefore can strip bark and dry husks without having to take them into their mouth at all.

The enemies of the LAGOMORPHA are many and man is not the least among them. Their habit therefore is that of hiding, augmented by well-developed ears and eyes and in many cases a communal warning system. This transmission of danger takes many forms, but the commonest and best known is that of thumping the ground with the hind legs.

The order shows peculiarities in its breeding and nutrition which divide it from other mammals, and these differences will be described more fully under the animals themselves.

THE RABBIT

Description

The rabbit is probably the only mammal familiar enough to pass without need of description. Its distinction from the brown hare is the smaller size, greyer colour and underground habit.

Range and Distribution

The rabbit is believed to have come originally from South West Europe and has now become widespread. It was introduced into Britain by the Romans or the Normans according to conflicting theories, and has successfully colonised all parts of the British Isles and Southern Ireland.

Habitat

The rabbit's habitat is catholic, both highland and lowland, coastal sand dunes and marshy fens, hedges and woods; and on higher ground it often makes its burrows amid rock and stone high up on mountain-sides.

Habits

The burrowing habit separates the rabbit from the hare, and likewise a community sense of well-developed and well-stocked warrens. It is a shy but inquisitive animal and in the main crepuscular, though it also goes out by day or night. The structure of rabbit holes and warrens is rather intricate with wide passing places, lined breeding holes and escape pop-holes. No bedding is brought into the holes, although the doe will sometimes line the breeding hole with tufts of her own fur.

The characteristic warning system of thumping with the hind feet is often noticed in warrens and is extremely audible underground.

Rabbits are not noticeably migratory and tend to remain in chosen areas.

Breeding

Bucks and does breed sporadically throughout the year as individuals but a definite breeding season is noticeable from January to June. This season is sharply defined because it is in January that the does are first able to become pregnant, while in July the decline in the buck's ability to serve the doe becomes noticeable. This condition is however the average one; indeterminate mating takes place fairly frequently outside these limits. As the female mates within a matter of hours of the birth of her young, litters are separated only by the duration of gestation period, which is about one calendar month. There is in addition a very high fertility rate and rabbits can breed in their first year even before they are fully grown. The average number of young born within a year to one adult doe is between ten and eleven.

There is a phenomenon in the breeding of rabbits and hares which is most interesting and peculiar to them alone. When litters in normal growth within the doe die before birth; instead of being stillborn they are completely reabsorbed into the tissue of the mother; the process takes only two days to complete and the doe will act exactly as though her litter has been properly born. When the absorption is complete she will conceive a second time. The proportion of litters conceived but never born is remarkably high, being well over half, and probably constitutes the highest single mortality factor. Litters can number between two and eight, with the larger number generally being born in the warmer months. They are born hairless and are blind and deaf. After ten days the ears can be independently moved and the eyes are open.

Feeding

Snails on occasion make the only exception to a

completely vegetarian diet, the quest of which so often puts the rabbit out of favour with the farmer and market gardener. A recently discovered characteristic of the feeding ways of rabbits is that their food is passed twice through the gut, the second passage enabling certain vitamins produced by bacterial action in the first passage to be absorbed into the animal's system. The familiar round

YOUNG RABBITS

droppings of the rabbit, often left in specially chosen latrine areas near the warren, are of a completely different nature from those of the first passage which are eaten again directly they emerge. It is the rabbit's method of grazing rather than the quantity it eats that is the reason for the damage it will cause to grassland; by nibbling the grass too closely they are apt to prevent its regeneration, so giving place only to the mosses which are typical of rabbit-infested pasture. Young trees are deformed by their taking the buds, and in hard weather are often killed by their habit of stripping the bark.

Voice

Though normally a silent animal the rabbit can be

provoked by fright into blood-curdling squeals, generally through the intervention of a stoat or when caught alive.

Enemies

Man must be their greatest enemy, but the food value of the rabbit makes it very sought after by all the carnivores, especially the fox, weasel and stoat; owls and buzzards take many of the young, whilst domestic dogs and cats account for many more.

THE HARES

General Note

The vague description ' a large rabbit ' sums up the hares; though all hares have black ear tips, proportionately longer hind legs, and live above ground. An essential difference is that of the young, for young hares are born with open eyes and full coat and they are active from birth. The leveret is a striking contrast from the helpless young rabbit. Far less is known of the breeding ways of hares than of rabbits; however it is known that reabsorption of conceived litters does take place in the same way, although it is believed to be to a lesser extent. Like rabbits refection takes place, droppings being eaten and passed a second time through the gut.

There are three different hares on the British list; these differ little except in colour and habitat: the Brown Hare, the Alpine or Blue Hare, and the Irish Hare.

THE BROWN HARE

Description

The typical British race of the Brown Hare is a darker animal than the continental one and it is

the largest of the British hares, often being over two feet long and over twice the weight of a rabbit. Its certain mark of distinction is the black on the upper surface of the tail. Its general colour is brownish-grey, paler beneath even to white under the belly. It moults twice a year in spring and autumn but has no white winter coat.

Distribution and Habitat

The Brown Hare is spread widely throughout Great Britain except on very high ground. It is a native animal but has been introduced into Orkney and Shetland and the Western Isles, and also into the Isle of Man and Ireland. Its habitat is the open country, field and farmland, where it is a familiar sight.

Habits

The most noticeable single feature about the hare is its behaviour in spring when its whole deportment becomes crazy and illustrates the expression ' mad as a March hare.' That this behaviour has a sexual origin is obvious because of the hostility of the males, the jacks, to each other and their tireless chase of the females, or does. However, there appears to be no fixed breeding season, for the Brown Hare is known to raise litters at most varied times. The animal lies up by day in a 'form,' which is simply a grass refuge in which it crouches, and it relies upon natural camouflage to escape detection. At dusk it leaves the form and returns at dawn, feeding during the night. In an endeavour to lose its scent on these journeys it invariably leaps great distances and doubles back on its tracks. The hare is a good swimmer and by no means afraid of water, and often will swim a fair distance if it leads to better foraging ground.

Breeding

Two to four litters a year are believed to be the average, and two to four seem to be the average number of leverets in each litter. There is no question of prolonged pairing for they mate promiscuously as do rabbits. Young leverets will make a form beside their parents, but are generally independent of them four weeks from birth.

Food

Hares are entirely vegetarian and their food is very varied including grasses, clover, kale, and all the root crops. Like rabbits they will also eat the bark of trees, especially young conifers. Though by no means the pest that rabbits are, they are pest enough for man to be their foe apart from their food value.

Voice

Hares have a danger transmission sound made by grinding the teeth, and also a series of grunts and yelps which are heard very frequently during the ' mad ' time. They have a scream like that of the rabbit when wounded or in great danger; and the sound made by sucking the back of one's hand is a device which will sometimes attract hares in the rutting season, and is akin to their own courting sounds.

Enemies

Leverets are naturally more easily taken by predatory birds and beasts, whilst man is the main enemy of the adult animal.

THE BLUE HARE

Description

The Blue Hare is smaller than the Brown Hare being about twenty inches long only. Like the stoat it changes to a white winter coat but retains the black tips to the ears, which are themselves shorter. The summer coat is a smoky brown or warm blue-grey with considerable variation, and in general it is a softer and woollier coat than that of the Brown Hare.

Distribution

The species is indigenous to Scotland and takes the place of the Brown Hare in the Highlands. Its form is often in the hard rock-crevices, and it is of necessity a hardy animal usually staying in the high ground in severe weather.

Enemies

To the list of enemies including man, should be added the Wild Cat and the Golden Eagle.

THE IRISH HARE

Description

This is the native hare of Ireland, and though larger than the Blue one is a slightly smaller animal than the Brown Hare; its average weight is some seven pounds and its length about twenty-three inches. Its coat is much redder than the Blue Hare's summer coat, but in winter the change is generally only partial, leaving haphazard patches of summer colouring against the white. In motion it gives the impression of being more graceful and longer-limbed than the Brown Hare which it so closely resembles in every other respect.

ORDER—RODENTIA

THE RODENTS

General Note

This Order is sub-divided into three groups of which two have British representatives: the *Myomorpha* which includes the mice and rats, the *Scivromorpha*, the squirrels, and the *Hystricomorpha*—this third one covers such animals as the porcupine, but does also include one introduced animal, the Coypu. The rodent order is the largest of the mammal groups and because of the great numbers of its members, helped by prolific breeding, it forms a large proportion of the whole mammal population. The Myomorpha is sub-divided three times again into the rats and mice, the voles and the dormice.

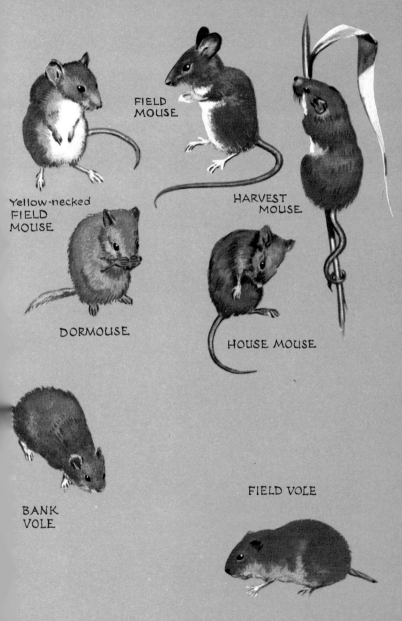

FIELD MOUSE

Yellow-necked FIELD MOUSE

HARVEST MOUSE

DORMOUSE

HOUSE MOUSE.

BANK VOLE

FIELD VOLE

PLATE 9

OF VOLES IN GENERAL

The voles are all burrowing animals, they are close-coated and short-tailed and their heads appear more rounded in profile so that they lack the pointed-nose look of mice and rats. Their eyes are small and beady. On the British list there are altogether some twenty races of voles, but most of these are island races, and it would be a biologist's work to tell them apart. They spring from three main types: the Bank Vole, the Field Vole and the Water Vole, a description of the habits of which should suffice to cover their ways in general. The large imported Musk Rat is in fact a vole and is closely related to the British Water Vole. Though not gregarious in the true sense of the word, it is not uncommon for voles to build up in numbers to the extent of causing a plague. Mystery surrounds the reason for these immense periodic increases and also for the crash which ends them. They all share the same enemies and it could be said that owls and weasels take the largest toll, though the day-flying hawks will seize them; and the island races are particularly vulnerable to gulls, hooded crows and the many predators which find them such good food.

THE BANK VOLE

Description

This animal is the most mouse-like of the voles, probably because its ears are a little bit more apparent than most. It is bright chestnut-brown in colour but lighter on the underpart; the upper surface of its tail is black. Its body length is about three and three-quarter inches making it somewhat smaller than the Field Vole, and it has a longer tail with a hairy tip, unlike that of the mice. Melanistic and albino variations have been known.

Distribution

It is generally spread throughout Great Britain, running well north into Scotland, but it is absent from Ireland and the outer islands where local races replace it. Its habitat differs somewhat from the Field Vole since it favours woodlands and hedgerows rather than open grassland.

Food

Its diet is general and varied but mainly vegetarian,

and includes buds, grasses, occasional insects, seeds, berries. It does not hoard food for the winter.

Habits

The Bank Vole is more agile than the Field Vole and is therefore more often seen abroad. Its habit is rather less burrowing although it builds the same type of passages under roots and leaves in hedgerows. It prefers somewhat drier places and does not hibernate.

Voice

A repertoire of quiet squeaks and grunts of a fairly continuous nature are typical of this animal.

Breeding

Its breeding months are March to September, and the number in the litter varies between three and six. The young are born naked and blind in a breeding nest made of grass, moss, and leaves, carefully made and domed above; voles will frequently use discarded birds'-nests.

THE SHORT-TAILED VOLE

Description

The Short-Tailed Vole is a typical vole type, a
small rufous-brown animal four inches long with a
very short tail; it has short rounded ears which
only just protrude from the fur, and a rounded head
which distinguish it easily from a mouse. The tail
is only a third of the body length. The hind feet
have six pads. The coat is thick and close and
darker above than beneath.

Habitat and Distribution

Like the Bank Vole the Short-Tailed Vole is well-
spread throughout Britain, although in outlying
islands its place is taken by local races, typical of
which is the Orkney Vole which resembles it
closely in every respect but that of size. Its habitats
are open fields and water meadows and cultivated
land and gardens. Much research has been done on
its movement, with particular reference to the great
plagues of these animals, the unaccountably vast
increases in their population built up over one, two

or three years and equally mysteriously ending with very great suddenness. Under such conditions they can be a considerable nuisance with their burrowing habits, particularly in re-afforestation areas.

Food

Their diet is vegetarian though they will occasionally take insects, and it has been calculated that this type of vole will eat its own weight of dry food in ten days. Its feeding habit is to feed and rest alternately throughout the day and night in short spells, resulting in about ten distinct forays in about twenty-four hours.

Habits

The whereabouts of the Short-Tailed Vole is typified by immense runs beneath grass and shallow underground tunnels which admirably protect the animal from the view of its many enemies. These runs have many escape routes and among them will be found the domed breeding nest which is covered with shredded grass. Much of the damage caused by voles is directly attributable to this burrowing habit; and the damage to roots is caused by the burrowing and the diet of the animals.

Breeding

Although the main breeding season lies between March and September, the male voles are potent a month earlier than this but the beginning of the breeding cycle is determined by the female. Litters number five or six and the young are born naked and blind. The life-expectancy of a vole is only some twelve months and those born early in the year will themselves breed that year and also early the next before they die. Towards the end of the summer the number in each litter drops and the period of gestation which is normally three weeks is considerably increased. Directly a litter is born the female vole can be reimpregnated for the following litter. The animals are sexually mature at a very early age; the females can breed as early as three weeks and the males when six weeks old.

THE WATER VOLE

Description

Often called the water rat, the Water Vole has a body length of seven and a half inches, a tail half that length. It is a dark brown, close-coated animal with beady eyes and ears almost lost in the fur. The nose is rounded in the typical vole fashion. The female is smaller than the male and rather greyer in colour.

Distribution

The animal is well spread throughout Great Britain, though absent from the islands and absent also from Ireland. Similar races exist overseas, principal among them being the Musk Rat of North America which has been introduced into this country in the past. Its habitat is almost entirely aquatic along the banks of ponds and rivers although it is not infrequently seen a fair distance from water.

Habits

The Water Vole gives the impression of being a very sociable animal and also of being somewhat short-sighted. It is often abroad in daytime and is an excellent swimmer, swimming both under water and on the surface. It does not hibernate although it makes large winter food stores against hard weather. Its burrows are familiar sights along the banks of rivers and streams and where the animals occur in large numbers a certain amount of damage can be done by this habit.

Food

Its vegetarian diet consists almost wholly of aquatic plants and seeds, willow shoots, beech-mast, and such items.

Breeding

The breeding period of the Water Vole is from March to late September, but as with the Short-Tailed Vole the females determine the start of the season. Litters generally number about five, and the fact that nursing females are often pregnant suggests that at least two litters are born each season and that like the other voles there is only a very short gap between them. Despite the water vole being a considerably larger animal than the rest it still has a life-span of only about a year or rather less. The breeding nest is a ball of rushes and grass, sometimes set in a hollow tree or a hole in a bank.

THE ORKNEY VOLE

Special mention should be made of the Orkney Vole for it is an exceptionally attractive animal and one which is very noticeably different from the mainland forms. In its island home it has developed a way of life and movement peculiar to its kind, the most noticeable feature of which is the tremendously long interlaced runs which the animal has formed in the heather.

In shape it is closer to the Short-Tailed Vole with well-hidden ears and a thick close coat. It has the same short tail and rounded muzzle, although it is a considerably larger animal.

OF MICE AND RATS
IN GENERAL

Though basically alike there are many physical characteristics which separate the mice and rats from the voles; they tend to be longer in the muzzle and their tails hairless or nearly so, their eyes tend to be larger and more obvious and their ears longer and naked. But it is in the diet that the greatest difference is found: whilst voles are almost entirely vegetarian, rats and mice are omnivorous. Their size alone makes their enemies many, and the frequency and efficiency of their breeding only just stems the tide of depredation caused by predators of all types. Every carnivorous animal and bird is against them, to say nothing of the hand of man, and they are even taken by large toads, grass snakes and adders. The rat by its size has less to fear, but will itself destroy not only mice but its own kind.

YELLOW-NECKED MOUSE

THE HOUSE MOUSE

Description

Well-known and endearing, the House Mouse is a great follower of man, and there can be few who have not had the opportunity of studying it in their own kitchen. Three to four inches long, with tail as long as its body, it is of greyish colour, darker above than below, but there is great variation in its colour, and it is from this species that the familiar White Mouse has been developed.

Distribution and Habitat

The House Mouse is spread widely throughout Great Britain; but in this spreading it has three distinct spheres of operation and in each of these it follows a different way of life. In its most familiar sense it is entirely a domestic animal living in houses. Its second type of habitat is that of a warehouse or farm; whilst its third and least obvious is that of a very common outdoor animal. In this last instance it has been found, surprisingly enough, to be in many country areas the third most common mammal in the fields during the summer months. One of the best examples of its communal life is to be found in ricks, which make a perfect harbour for it, offering it protection from predators, warmth, nest-material and food without moving. Under such conditions it will multiply at fantastic rates and cause infestation of the rick. Wheat ricks appear to be most popular with the House Mouse.

Habits and Characteristics

An agile cunning animal which can climb nearly anything and jump prodigious distances, which can creep from its hole and move silently about a room —there is little about the House Mouse that is not already well-known—nor is there about the human reactions at the sight of it!

Breeding

Because of its three distinct ways of life the breeding cycles and frequency of the House Mouse are very variable indeed; for the whole average of the species one might say four to five litters per year, these litters would number five or six in each and some-times as many as twelve. The young are born blind and naked, but are self-sufficient in fourteen days. Mice in human homes tend, however, to have a lower breeding rate compared with those in, for instance, warehouses which might raise eight litters in a year. Those in ricks can produce as many as ten litters each year, making it possible for an individual female to raise as many as thirty to fifty-five young within twelve months. An interesting point is that mice which make their homes in cold stores in which meat is kept, and where they live with no light and under Arctic temperatures, raise larger and more frequent litters than those in domestic houses; whilst the animals themselves tend to be slightly larger. House Mice frequently have communal nests, especially when colonising a rick, and under these conditions of fast multiplication the female will become pregnant immediately after the birth of each litter.

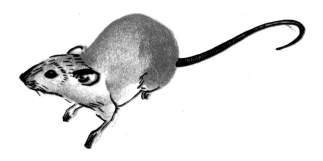

THE FIELD MOUSE

Description

The Field Mouse is one of the commonest of British mammals. Its body is about three and a half inches long with a tail nearly as long. It has a pointed snout, is yellowish-brown above and white underneath, with the two colours distinctly divided; there is a bright buff marking on the chest which is very variable in different races of the same animal.

Distribution

There are very large numbers of identifiably different local species of Field Mouse spread all over the country, but so similar are they in aspect that it is the biologist's work to separate them. The common Field Mouse is widely spread over Europe including Great Britain, though it is less numerous in Ireland.

Habits

Field Mice are primarily nocturnal. They seem to have no migratory tendency and move only the shortest distances from their base, which is typified by burrows under grass roots and leaves. They are very agile and great jumpers. Though they are inactive in winter they do not properly hibernate, and often tend to come indoors in this season, when they are frequently mistaken for the House Mouse. Despite the burrowing habit the Field Mouse often makes use of dry stone walls and crevices in outbuildings, where a reasonably safe house may be made. It is tame, sociable, and seems to be short-sighted and is therefore easily caught in the hand. Although the breeding nest is frequently in a burrow, it is apt also to use deserted birds'-nests and to form communal stores where a great variety of food is kept.

BLACK or SHIP RAT

BROWN
RAT

WATER
VOLE

PLATE 10

Food

The Field Mouse's diet is very varied, and though seldom a big nuisance to agriculture it certainly is to market-gardening; generally it is the animal responsible for eating newly-sown peas, beans, etc., and ripe strawberries. The communal winter food stores contain nuts, haws, and seeds of all kinds.

Breeding

The breeding nest of the Field Mouse is in the form of a ball about six inches in diameter with a three-inch breeding chamber inside and is generally at the end of a long burrow. The breeding chamber sometimes incorporates the food store. As with most small rodents the males are fertile four weeks before the breeding season begins, which lasts from March to November with a decided peak in the summer months. Litters vary between two and nine and average about five. The gestation period is twenty-five days. Females are reimpregnated directly after the birth of the previous litter; nursing mothers therefore are pregnant with a new litter which is born directly after weaning. The young can breed after two or three months and generally will raise a total of six litters in their lifetime which lasts generally rather less than one year.

THE HARVEST MOUSE

Description

The Harvest Mouse is the smallest rodent and the second smallest British mammal, the smallest of all being the Pigmy Shrew. The body length is under two and a half inches, the tail is as long as the body and prehensile at the tip. Upper parts are coloured yellowish or rufous with a hard line dividing that and the white underparts. The coat is thick and soft. The muzzle is short for a mouse and the ears are short and rounded. Young Harvest Mice are greyer than their parents, taking on the adult colouring at the approach of winter.

Distribution and Habitat

Up to a few hundred years ago this animal was well spread throughout Great Britain; now it is confined mainly to the South East of England. It is still very numerous on the continent where it occasionally constitutes a plague and can do very considerable damage to cereal crops. Its habitat is pasture and open country and hedgerows, and it is by no means confined to cornfields as its name might imply.

Habits

It is mainly diurnal: its typical attitude is that of climbing grass and corn stems where it will be seen to use its prehensile tail as an additional foot. It will scale the thinnest stems to cut off ears and seeds at the top. It burrows however and sleeps extensively in the winter; at this time of the year also it will frequently be found in ricks. The most engaging of its habits is its building of a summer nursery, which is in the form of a woven hollow ball about four inches in diameter, set above ground in corn or bushes. There is no apparent opening in the ball for the animal forces its way in and out and raises its young there.

Food

Grain and seeds of all kinds. This mouse uses its unique climbing ability to take insects from the tops of stems. It also makes large winter stores.

Breeding

The breeding ways and cycles of this animal have not been watched so closely as some of the others, but it is known to have litters numbering four to nine which are born blind and naked, and to rear several litters in the course of a year. It is also known that when living in ricks it will raise young in the winter months as well as in the normal summer breeding season.

Voice

The Harvest Mouse has a well-known chirping voice which could easily be mistaken for that of a small bird.

THE BLACK RAT

Description

The Black Rat which is also known as the ' ship rat '
is a relatively small rat, about seven inches long,
with a tail rather longer than its body. It has a
pointed snout and a thick and glossy coat, blue-grey
or black in colour. The ears are naked and pink and
the feet and tail are of the same colour. It is not
unattractive by comparison with the brown one.

Habitat and Distribution

The Black Rat is well spread throughout Europe
and is the older of the two British species of rat,
having been imported into Great Britain and Ireland
about the fourteenth century, presumably by ships.
It has taken up its abode in warehouses, stores,
granaries, etc., and is seldom far away from the
activities of man. It is interesting that the House
Mouse and the rats have definitely attached themselves to man as providing their best means of
making a livelihood. Their existence and pro-
creation is directly dependent upon man's own food
stores and the waste he throws about.

Habits

The Black Rat is a great climber and more agile than the Brown Rat; it is also of a milder disposition and is the wild and natural version of the domestic White Rat, the children's pet.

Food

Entirely omnivorous and cannibalistic, it is difficult to conceive of any matter which can be eaten at all which rats will not eat with relish. Their voracious quest for food is in fact a considerable economic factor, and brings effective means of rat destruction constantly under survey.

Breeding

The breeding nest of the Black Rat is a haphazard collection of straw, papers, rags, etc., torn from wherever it can find them. The litter generally numbers seven to eight and five to six litters are produced each year. The young are born naked, blind and deaf.

THE BROWN RAT

Description

The Brown Rat is a much larger and considerably less attractive animal than the Black Rat. It is greyish in colour, lighter underneath than above and suffused with a dark brown. Compared with the Black Rat it has a shorter muzzle and comparatively shorter tail, which is generally less than the body length.

Distribution and Habitat

The Brown Rat was introduced some four hundred years later than the Black Rat, but has quickly replaced this species by domination. Its range now extends throughout Great Britain and Ireland and even to the farthermost islands. Its habitat extends anywhere close to human habitation, although like the House Mouse and unlike the Black Rat it has a considerable outdoor distribution. A fairly constant water supply is necessary to it, and although mice can often subsist where no source of water is apparent, this is not the case with the Brown Rat.

Food

Like the Black Rat it is completely omnivorous and a cannibal. However it has the added nuisance value of being extremely dangerous to poultry and will wreak havoc among clamped vegetables and in granaries wherever it is not kept in check.

Habits

The Brown Rat is too familiar an animal for description, and stories concerning its cunning and its tricks are legion. It seems to have linked its fortunes inseparably with man, living on his chickens and their eggs, his food stores and vegetables, and even taking refuge in his sewers. The rat has a great nuisance value commercially and medically; it is a disease-spreader not only on its own account but through the fleas it carries. It is however an engaging animal and the study of it will always bring its rewards.

Breeding

The Brown Rat seems to have no set season for breeding and the pattern appears as a breeding period followed by a rest period throughout the year. There is however an overall tendency which forms a peak between March and June, particularly among rats of an outdoor habit; but as with the House Mouse environment dictates the rate. A young rat will reach sexual maturity within three to four months and has a life span of about eighteen months. It will probably raise four to five litters in a year and the litters will number somewhere between four and ten. The young are born deaf, blind and naked after a three-week period of gestation.

THE DORMOUSE

Description

Sometimes. called the Dosing Mouse, this might be
described as the most beautiful little animal in
Britain. In character it bridges the gap between
the mice and the squirrels, but being biologically
separate from both it has been put into a family of
its own. It is a compact little animal, thick-coated,
short-muzzled and long-whiskered, with prominent
black eyes, and is of a biscuit colour darker above
than below with the throat nearly white. Young
dormice are greyer. The tail is nearly as long as the
body and thickly furred. The body without the tail
is about three inches long, and though no larger than
the mice it gives the impression of being more
compactly made.

Distribution and Habitat

Its range extends all over Europe except the northern Arctic areas; however, it is absent or extremely rare in Scotland and is unknown in Ireland. In England is it widely spread except in the Eastern Counties. Its typical habitat is the woodland and hedgerow, and like the squirrel it is seldom far from trees.

Habits

The Dormouse going about its business has much more the look of a squirrel than that of a mouse; all its gestures and movements have the squirrel trend, in particular the characteristic attitude of sitting up with a nut in the forepaws. It is nocturnal and spends the day in a state of such torpor and somnolence that the creature might be believed dead. The heart beat becomes almost imperceptible and the temperature low. This daytime sleep is passed in a small round nest just large enough to accommodate the animal, generally with a hole in the side, and made from bark strips, grass and leaves and lined with finer material. These nests will be found in thick grass or hedge-bottoms, but are often fairly high up in bushes. The winter nest to which the animal retires in autumn is generally either underground or under very thick cover. In this nest winter stores are made. Winter hibernation is not complete for there are short feeding breaks in it.

The sleep however is so intense that no breathing is detectable; the creature becomes quite cold and stiff, and its rate of metabolism completely retarded. At the end of hibernation in April it is about one-half the weight that it was in October when it had stored up fat ready for the long sleep. It is this very low metabolic rate for half of their lives which indicates that Dormice are longer lived than the other small rodents and may have a life span of two or three years.

Food

Hazelnuts are probably the favourite food, the kernels being extracted from a hole gnawed through the shell. It will eat also whitethorn berries, fruit, seeds and insects.

Breeding

The Dormouse's nursery nest is twice the size of the day nest. Litters number three to seven and several litters are born during the summer. The gestation period is about four weeks, the young being born blind and naked.

THE FAT OR EDIBLE DORMOUSE

Description

Much larger than the common Dormouse and even more squirrel-like is the Fat Dormouse. Greyish in colour it is over six inches long in the body with a tail of the same length, but densely furred like that of a squirrel and with a curiously brittle end which is often shed when the animal seeks to escape from a hold on the tail, in the fashion of a lizard.

Distribution and Habitat

The Fat Dormouse is essentially a European species and was carefully nurtured by the Romans for food. At the end of the last century they were imported into this country by the late Lord Rothschild and released at Tring. Although thriving well and increasing, their range is even now restricted only to this local area in Buckinghamshire and Hertfordshire, where their habitat is the same as the Common Dormouse. It must have the most localised range of any British mammal.

Habits

Nocturnal and very arboreal, as with the Common Dormouse. It is a dynamic creature, leaping about in low branches and seldom seen to use the ground. Its nests follow the same pattern and likewise its hibernating ways. At the onset of autumn this animal is excessively fat in readiness for the winter sleep.

Food

Because of its larger size it may well take a greater variety than the smaller animal; and in addition to fruit, nuts, seeds and berries it is said to take small birds, fledglings and eggs.

Breeding

It is believed to breed in mid-summer, with smaller litters of two to four young, and possibly fewer litters in the season.

THE COYPU

Description

A spectacular and unmistakable animal is the Coypu, looking not unlike a long-coated, two-foot rat, with eighteen inches of scaly hairless tail, weighing up to twenty pounds. Its ears are small and rounded and its whiskers long; its hind feet are webbed. Its general colour is darkish brown and the coat, which is rich and thick, is known to the furrier as ' nutria.'

Distribution

The Coypu is a native of South America and was imported here about thirty years ago in the boom time of the fur-farm and gained a foothold through escapes. It is semi-aquatic in habit and made strongholds in certain lakeside areas and in parts of Norfolk where it became well established in the denser reed-beds.

Habits

The animal is diurnal and nocturnal alike, and though it burrows, the holes are of no great depth, and the incidental damage which it has caused is far less than was expected, following the earlier example of the Musk Rat. Its breeding nests are built in the sedges and made of reeds. The period of gestation is long, being about 120 days, and litters average about five young. These young are extremely quick to develop, leaving the nest when only a day old.

RED SQUIRREL

GREY SQUIRREL

FAT or EDIBLE DORMOUSE

PLATE 11

THE RED SQUIRREL

Description

Strikingly beautiful with its red coat and sandy tail and ear tufts, large black eyes and quick engaging movements, the Red Squirrel is an animal often seen and easily watched. The body-length is about eight inches with a tail the same length. The tail is very thickly furred, the fur spreading sideways so that it has a flat appearance like a ribbon of hair. There is a partial spring and a complete autumn moult, leaving the animal rather greyer and browner for the winter, during which season the soles of its hands and feet are haired. The thick luxuriant growth of hair on the tail is buff in autumn, gradually bleaching out to near-white, the hair itself becoming more sparse until in autumn again just prior to the moult, the tail is at its thinnest.

Distribution

The very pale sandy colour of the Red Squirrel's tail marks it as the British race, and differentiates it from the same basic species which is spread widely across Europe and Asia and as far north as the tree-line. In Great Britain its numbers have fluctuated tremendously in the last few hundred years, swaying in places between abundance and near extinction.. At present it is commonest in the North and West of the British Isles, the area where it is scarce or absent being in the South Eastern Counties, including the Midlands and East Anglia. It is now plentiful in Ireland, having once been practically extinct there. From what is known it is not believed to be true that the imported Grey Squirrel has affected its numbers to a measurable extent, and where their ranges overlap they seem to be able to

live together happily. The habitat of the squirrels is entirely woodland, preferring trees of an established size.

Habits

Squirrels are always abroad by day. They are renowned climbers and branch runners, often using their outstretched limbs as planes for their longest leaps. Their whole life centres around trees for their escape and hiding and for their food, their exercise and their courtship. Though they are often seen foraging on the ground beneath, it is the tree itself and that which it provides which is the whole life of the squirrel. The nest or ' drey ' is a large structure of sticks, leaves, bark and moss, not unlike a magpie's nest, but lacking an entrance. Like many of the mice the squirrel pushes in through the side of the nest. The drey is the squirrel's home throughout the year as well as the nursery nest. Both Red and Grey Squirrels are excellent swimmers when need arises.

Food

Food consists of all vegetable matter, nuts, fruit, pine-cones, beech-mast, seeds, bark and woodland fungi, as well as insects, young birds and their eggs. The Red Squirrel is a nuisance in re-afforestation areas where its habit of barking the leading shoots of young trees causes them to grow deformed so that the timber will be knotted and its straight-grained quality will be lost. Squirrels make proverbially large winter stores, favouring in particular the hazelnut when available.

Breeding

For so common an animal surprisingly little is known. Pregnant and nursing mothers are found right through from December to the following autumn, and it seems that there are two distinct peaks of breeding, one in early spring and the other in late summer. Litters number three or four blind and naked young which remain in the drey for two or three weeks. The period of gestation is believed to be four to five weeks, and the males are known to be fertile from November to early August.

Voice

The excited chattering, yickering and barking of the squirrel is a well-known woodland sound and is not infrequently mistaken for the quarrelsome under-tones of jays and magpies.

THE GREY SQUIRREL

Description

As the common squirrel of the Home Counties and always out by day this animal will be well-known. The length of its body is nearly a foot and its weight vastly greater than that of the Red Squirrel. It is, however, a most attractively marked animal with a speckled grey coat with lighter front and ochre patches about the head. The many coloured hairs that go into it have the effect of making the tail paler grey by contrast, particularly as the longer hairs pick up the light. It has the same large black eyes but lacks the characteristic ear tufts of the Red Squirrel.

Distribution

The Grey Squirrel is a native of the American Eastern States. Introductions have taken place here in the last eighty years over fairly wide areas, and the animals have increased and consolidated everywhere but in East Anglia. Ireland has been colonised; but they have not penetrated far into

Scotland, and are far more numerous in the South West and Midlands than elsewhere, with isolated pockets where they are especially plentiful. They may be seen in numbers anywhere from Kent to Dorset, northwards and through the Midlands where they thin out, becoming more numerous again in Lancashire and Cheshire. Counties as far apart as South Devon and Yorkshire are well populated with Grey Squirrels. Their habitat is woodland, with perhaps a greater preference for deciduous woods than pine, which, where they occur, seem to be more favoured by the Red Squirrels.

Habits

The habits of the Grey Squirrel are so little different from those of the native Red Squirrel there is little that can be added. However, there is much more known about the breeding habits of this animal which may throw a little light on those of the Red Squirrel as well.

Breeding

The span of the breeding season is from January to August with two noticeable peaks, April and again in July. The first peak represents litters born to older parents; the second peak includes as well younger parents born in the previous year. Young squirrels which have been born even in the earliest part of the early peak will not breed again in the same year. Unlike other rodents there is no mating until after the weaning of the litter, and this probably accounts for the complete lack of pregnant females in May and probably indicates that two litters a year is the total expected for each pair. There is no breeding from August to January, though surprisingly enough males are fertile at that time. It is believed however that males are not fertile till their second year. The young are born blind and naked and the average number in a litter is two to five, and there is a gap of about three months between successive litters in the same year.

INTRODUCTION TO
THE WHALES

Because they are true mammals, and because they are so often seen around our shores, the whales should be mentioned, despite all the obvious physical differences which separate them from the wild animals of the land.

Whales are completely aquatic, never coming ashore voluntarily, in spite of the occasional stranding which takes place. Because of this completely waterborne existence their size and weight is far less restricted. This is illustrated by the fact that the largest of them all, the Blue Whale, is the largest animal of any kind ever known to have inhabited the earth, reaching lengths of over a hundred feet and weights of over a hundred and twenty tons. Closely related to it, however, are the smaller dolphins and porpoises whose ways of breeding and structure are all alike, and they are all grouped under the same Order, the CETACEA. The list of those which have wandered into British waters is vast because the sea presents them with a medium of unhampered travel, and therefore most of the whale species of the world have at one time or another been reported here.

It is not surprising that in form the whales are so similar to fish, because both have evolved a shape suitable to water movement, a shape which is essentially streamlined and with certain other adaptations to a specialised way of life. A big difference between them, however, lies in the position of the tail fins or flukes of the CETACEANS which are always horizontal, whilst the tail fin of a fish is vertical. The skeleton structure of the CETACEANS follows exactly the formula of an ordinary terrestrial mammal in that the bone groups are present, the fore limbs having adapted themselves into flippers, and even the hind limbs which are completely invisible externally being present in the shape of minute remains of bone structure in an entirely rudimentary form under the skin. Whales breath air and the nostrils are developed into blow-holes on the top of the head, enabling the animal to breathe freely with the bulk of the body submerged. The familiar spout of the whale is caused simply by exhaling; it is not solid water but condensation and water taken up by the force of its outward breath when emitted under the surface. The whole system of the animal is adapted for resistance to great pressure changes and for the ability to hold its breath for anything up to two hours on end.

The whales are subdivided into two groups, the ODONTOCETI, the Toothed Whales, and the MYSTICETI, the Whalebone Whales. The

BLUE WHALE

former group includes all the porpoises and dolphins which are Carnivores living mostly on fish, and the largest of them is the Sperm Whale which measures up to sixty feet in length. The biggest whales of the sea however belong to the whalebone group, the Rorquals; their jaws are generally scoop-shaped and filled with vast combs of baleen or whalebone through which their food, the shrimp-like ' krill,' is filtered. Although most of the species in this group have been reported in our waters at one time or another, they seldom approach closer than the hundred-fathom line, and it is the Toothed Whales which we are much more likely to see.

The breeding cycle of whales differs little from one species to another, and the processes are fundamentally identical to any other mammal. If we consider the Blue Whale, the largest of all, it will give us the most spectacular example. The Blue Whale's gestation period is only about twelve months, but the baby Blue Whale is born with the impressive dimensions of twenty-five feet in length and a weight of fifteen tons! It is suckled for six

BOTTLE-NOSED WHALE

months, and the mother will breed again in a
further six months.

All whales are gregarious, often forming schools
of a great size, and in many of the instances of
strandings on our coasts large schools have been
involved. From a long list of possibilities there are
several species frequently enough reported to make
them worth special mention, and all of these are of
the toothed type.

Note: Because of the ever-present possibility of stranding
of all kinds of whales, anybody finding one should
contact without delay the British Museum of Natural
History, South Kensington, London, so that records
may be kept up to date and every opportunity given for
study.

THE COMMON PORPOISE

Description

This is the smallest and also the commonest British whale. Its length is very seldom as great as six feet, and never more. Its snout is not beaked like that of the dolphin but is rather blunt, and its dorsal fin low and wide at the base. Its colour is black above, variably grading to white below.

Distribution

Common Porpoises are widely spread throughout the North Atlantic; their migrations bring them into British waters in summer, and they are commonest from then on until the autumn. Porpoises often travel far up the estuaries of the larger rivers and are therefore the species most frequently seen from land.

Habits

The Porpoise is an active, dynamic animal which seems to delight in its ability to leap high in the air and disport itself in the waves. It is inquisitive and sociable to shipping and extremely gregarious.

Food

Its food consists almost exclusively of fish; whiting and herring, mackerel and bass being the principal ones.

Breeding

Pairing takes place in the late summer and the young is born the following summer after a gestation period of eight to nine months. The young is very large in proportion to the size of the mother, being at birth nearly half her length.

THE COMMON DOLPHIN

Description

This is a larger animal and one of the most beauti-
fully proportioned of the whales. It is recognised at
once from the Porpoise by the beak which is about
five inches long, and by the higher and backward
curved dorsal fin. Its colour is browner and rather
more varied in its gradation from black to white.

Distribution

Its range is in warmer waters than the Porpoise,
farther South in the Atlantic and Mediterranean,
migrating North to become quite common in the
English Channel and the Irish Sea in late summer
and autumn.

Food

Fish, cuttle fish and squids, the main fish diet being mackerel, pilchards and herrings.

Breeding

The young are born in early summer well before the animals reach our coastal waters, visiting summer schools having the young with the adults.

THE WHITE-BEAKED DOLPHIN

Description

The adult of this species is about nine feet and one of the larger Dolphin species. The beak is shorter and broader than that of the Common Dolphin and is startlingly white against the black of the brow and upper parts of the body. Both upper and lower surfaces of the flippers and flukes are black.

Distribution

In British waters it is most frequently seen in the North Sea and seldom if ever in the Channel. It occurs however up the Atlantic coasts of Ireland and Scotland and occasionally in the Irish Sea. Migrations appear to be northward in summer and southward in winter. It is noticeably less gregarious than the Common Dolphin and schools seldom number more than thirty.

COMMON
DOLPHIN

COMMON
PORPOISE

PILOT WHALE,
BLACKFISH or CAA'ING
WHALE

White-beaked
DOLPHIN

GRAMPUS or
KILLER WHALE

PLATE 12

THE GRAMPUS OR KILLER WHALE

Description

This is the largest of the Dolphins and of a most striking and characteristic pattern of black and white. Males of the species are often twice the length of the females and are easily identified by the great height of the dorsal fin. Old bulls, which can be thirty feet in length, will have a tall, straight-sided dorsal fin as high as six feet. The young males, however, and females have a lower, backward curved dorsal fin, more like a conventional Dolphin shape. The flippers are round and paddle-shaped and there is no beak.

Distribution

Killer Whales are found in all seas throughout the world: though infrequent visitors can be met with in our waters at any time of the year and reports of them are fairly regular.

Habits and Food

This is one of the fiercest animals in the sea, schools of them often attacking the larger and more defence-less Whalebone Whales and taking heavy toll of all types of fish, porpoises and seals. In the latter case its habit is frequently to break the ice-floes from below by an upheaval of its back and to take the seals as they fall. In this way it has also been known to take man. They seldom form large schools as do other whales and are more often seen in a small party consisting of one old bull and several cows, or single lone bulls. The young are born in November and December.

Note: A look at the check-list will show all the whales which have occurred in the past, and may well occur again. There are other species as yet unseen in our waters against which there is no physical barrier to their possible appearance. Whales should be watched for and reported whenever seen, and anybody habitually by the sea coast would be interested to study ' Stranded Whales and Turtles ' published by the Natural History Museum, London, not only as a guide to the animals themselves but to the procedure for reporting strandings.

THE PILOT WHALE

Description

The Pilot Whale is up to twenty-five feet long with a characteristic rounded head forming a high brow. It is black, hence the name Black Fish, except for a small patch of white or light grey on the throat. The dorsal fin is broad-based and low; the flukes widespread and the flippers long and pointed.

Distribution

It is found throughout the North Atlantic, being most frequently seen around the Faroes, Orkney, Shetland and the North of Scotland.

Habits

It is an extremely gregarious animal and schools of them number several hundred. This species was at one time taken in large numbers by the simple process of driving it ashore with a small fleet of boats, and for its size it is particularly rich in oil. The young are born in July and August.

CHECKLIST OF BRITISH MAMMALS

INSECTIVORA

Erinaceus europaeus Linnaeus, 1758	Hedgehog
Talpa europaea Linnaeus, 1758	Mole
Sorex minutus Linnaeus, 1766	Pigmy Shrew
Sorex araneus castaneus Jenyns, 1838	Common Shrew
Sorex araneus fretalis Miller, 1909	Jersey Red-toothed Shrew
Sorex granti Barrett-Hamilton & Hinton, 1913	Islay Shrew
Neomys fodiens bicolor Shaw, 1791	Water Shrew
Crocidura suaveolens cassiteridum Hinton, 1924	Scilly Islands Shrew
Crocidura russula peta Montagu & Pickford, 1923	Guernsey White-toothed Shrew

CHIROPTERA

Rhinolophus ferrumequinum insulanus Barrett-Hamilton, 1910	Greater Horseshoe Bat
Rhinolophus hipposideros minutus Montagu, 1808	Lesser Horseshoe Bat
Myotis mystacinus Kuhl, 1819	Whiskered Bat
Myotis nattereri Kuhl, 1818	Natterer's Bat
Myotis bechsteini Kuhl, 1818	Bechstein's Bat
Myotis daubentoni Kuhl, 1819	Daubenton's, or Water Bat
Eptesicus serotinus Schreber, 1774	Serotine Bat
Nyctalus leisleri Kuhl, 1818	Leisler's Bat
Nyctalus noctula Schreber, 1774	Noctule
Pipistrellus pipistrellus Schreber, 1774	Pipistrelle
Barbastella barbastellus Schreber, 1774	Barbastelle
Plecotus auritus Linnaeus, 1758	Long-eared Bat

CARNIVORA

Vulpes vulpes crucigera Bechstein, 1789	Fox
Martes martes Linnaeus, 1758	Pine Marten
Mustela erminea hibernica Thomas & Barrett-Hamilton, 1895	Irish Stoat
Mustela erminea stabilis Barrett Hamilton, 1904	Stoat
Mustela erminea ricinae Miller, 1907	Islay Stoat
Mustela nivalis Linnaeus, 1758	Weasel
Mustela putorius anglius Pocock, 1936	Polecat
Mustela putorius caledoniae Tetley, 1939	Scottish Polecat
Meles meles Linnaeus, 1758	Badger
Lutra lutra Linnaeus, 1758	Otter
Felis silvestris grampia Miller, 1907	Scottish Wild Cat
Halichoerus grypus Fabricius, 1791	Grey Seal
Phoca vitulina Linnaeus, 1758	Common Seal

UNGULATA

Cervus elaphus scoticus Lönnberg, 1906	Red Deer
Dama dama Linnaeus, 1758	Fallow Deer
[1]*Capreolus capreolus* Linnaeus, 1758	Roe Deer
[2]*Hydropotes inermis* Swinhoe, 1870	Chinese Water Deer
[2]*Muntiacus reevesi* Ogilby, 1839	Chinese Muntjac or Barking Deer
[2]*Cervus nippon nippon* Temminck, 1838	Japanese Sika
[2]*Cervus nippon hortulorum* Swinhoe, 1864	Manchurian Sika

[1] A British race has been differentiated as *C. c. thotti* Lönnberg, 1910, but it does not seem to be distinguishable from the typical race. Specimens of the Siberian race, *C. c. pygargus* Pallas, 1771, have escaped from captivity and are said to have established themselves wild in Northamptonshire and Bedfordshire.

[2] Introduced.

LAGOMORPHA

Lepus europaeus occidentalis de Winton, 1898	Brown Hare
Lepus timidus hibernicus Bell, 1837	Irish Hare
Lepus timidus scoticus Hilzheimer, 1906	Scottish Mountain or Blue Hare
Oryctolagus cuniculus Linnaeus, 1758	Rabbit

RODENTIA

Sciurus vulgaris leucourus Kerr, 1792	Red Squirrel
[2]*Sciurus carolinensis* Gmelin, 1788	Grey Squirrel
[2]*Glis glis* Linnaeus, 1766	Fat or Edible Dormouse
Muscardinus avellanarius Linnaeus, 1758	Dormouse
Micromys minutus soricinus Hermann 1780	Harvest Mouse
Apodemus sylvaticus sylvaticus Linnaeus, 1758	Field Mouse
[1]*Apodemus sylvaticus hebridensis* de Winton, 1895	Hebridean Field Mouse
Apodemus sylvaticus butei Hinton, 1914	Bute Field Mouse
Apodemus sylvaticus cumbrae Hinton, 1914	Cumbrae Field Mouse
Apodemus sylvaticus maclean Hinton, 1914	Mull Field Mouse
Apodemus sylvaticus fiolagan Hinton, 1914	Arran Field Mouse

[1] These island races of Field Mouse and Vole have been distinguished by such small differences that, though technically valid, it is doubtful whether most of these subspecific names should really have been bestowed at all.

[2] Introduced.

Apodemus sylvaticus tirae Montagu, 1923	Tiree Field Mouse
Apodemus sylvaticus tural Montagu, 1923	Islay Field Mouse
Apodemus sylvaticus ghia Montagu, 1923	Gigha Field Mouse
Apodemus sylvaticus larus Montagu, 1923	Jura Field Mouse
Apodemus sylvaticus nesiticus Warwick, 1940	Mingulay Field Mouse
Apodemus flavicollis hirtensis Barrett-Hamilton, 1899	St. Kilda Field Mouse
Apodemus flavicollis wintoni Barrett-Hamilton, 1900	Yellow-necked Field Mouse
Apodemus flavicollis fridariensis Kinnear, 1906	Fair Isle Field Mouse
Apodemus flavicollis hamiltoni Hinton, 1914	Rum Field Mouse
Apodemus flavicollis granti Hinton, 1914	Shetland Field Mouse
Apodemus flavicollis thuleo Hinton, 1919	Foula Field Mouse
Rattus rattus Linnaeus, 1758	Black or Ship Rat
Rattus norvegicus Berkenhout, 1769	Brown Rat
[1]*Mus musculus* Linnaeus, 1758	House Mouse
Clethrionomys glareolus britannicus Miller, 1900	Bank Vole
Clethrionomys glareolus skomerensis Barrett-Hamilton, 1903	Skomer Vole
Clethrionomys (?) *glareolus alstoni* Barrett-Hamilton & Hinton, 1913	Mull Vole
Clethrionomys rufocanus caesarius Miller, 1908	Jersey Vole

[1] A form, *Mus muralis* Barrett-Hamilton, 1899, from St. Kilda, was described as being larger than and differently coloured from the House Mouse. It was probably only an island race at most, but seems now to be extinct.

Clethrionomys (?) *rufocanus erica* Barrett-Hamilton & Hinton, 1913	Raasay Vole
Arvicola terrestris amphibius Linnaeus 1758	Water Vole= Water "Rat"
Arvicola terrestris reta Miller, 1910	Highland Water Vole
Arvicola terrestris brigantium Thomas, 1928	Yorkshire Water Vole
Microtus arvalis sarnius Miller, 1909	Guernsey Vole
[1]*Microtus orcadensis orcadensis* Millais, 1904	Orkney Vole
Microtus orcadensis sandayensis Millais, 1905	Sanday Vole
Microtus orcadensis westrae Miller, 1908	Westray Vole
Microtus orcadensis ronaldshaiensis Hinton, 1913	Ronaldshay Vole
Microtus orcadensis rousaiensis Hinton, 1913	Rousay Vole
Microtus agrestis hirtus Bellamy, 1839	Field Vole
Microtus agrestis neglectus Jenyns, 1841	Scottish Field Vole
Microtus agrestis exsul Miller, 1908	Hebridean Vole
Microtus agrestis mial Barrett-Hamilton & Hinton, 1913	Eigg Vole
Microtus agrestis luch Barrett-Hamilton & Hinton, 1913	Muck Vole
Microtus agrestis macgillivrayi Barrett-Hamilton & Hinton, 1913	Islay Vole
Microtus agrestis fiona Montagu, 1922	Gigha Vole
[2]*Myocastor coypus* Molina, 1782	Nutria or Coypu

[1] These island races of Vole have been distinguished by such small differences that, though technically valid, it is doubtful whether most of these subspecific names should really have been bestowed at all.

[2] Introduced from South America.

CETACEA

Eubalaena glacialis Borowski, 1781	North Atlantic Right Whale
Megaptera novaeangliae Borowski, 1781	Humpback Whale
Balaenoptera physalus Linnaeus, 1758	Common Rorqual or Fin Whale
Balaenoptera acutorostrata Lacepede, 1804	Lesser Rorqual or Pike Whale
Balaenoptera musculus Linnaeus, 1758	Blue Whale
Balaenoptera borealis Lesson, 1828	Sei Whale
Physeter catodon Linnaeus, 1758	Sperm Whale or Cachalot
Hyperoodon ampullatus Forster, 1770	Bottle-nosed Whale
Ziphius cavirostris G. Cuvier, 1823	Cuvier's Beaked Whale
Mesoplodon bidens Sowerby, 1804	Sowerby's Whale
Mesoplodon mirus True, 1913	True's Whale
Monodon monoceros Linnaeus, 1758	Narwhal
Delphinapterus leucas Pallas, 1776	White Whale or Beluga
Globicephala melaena Traill, 1809	Blackfish, Pilot Whale or Caa'ing Whale
Grampus griseus G. Cuvier, 1812	Risso's Dolphin
Orcinus orca Linnaeus, 1758	Killer Whale or Grampus
Pseudorca crassidens Owen, 1846	False Killer
Phocaena phocoena Linnaeus, 1758	Porpoise
Tursiops truncatus Montagu, 1821	Bottle-nosed Dolphin
Lagenorhynchus albirostris Gray, 1846	White-beaked Dolphin
Lagenorhynchus acutus Gray, 1828	White-sided Dolphin
Delphinus delphis Linnaeus, 1758	Common Dolphin
Stenella styx Gray, 1846	Euphrosyne Dolphin

LONG-TAILED FIELD MOUSE